THE LEAD INDUSTRY OF WENSLEYDALE AND SWALEDALE
Vol 1 The Mines

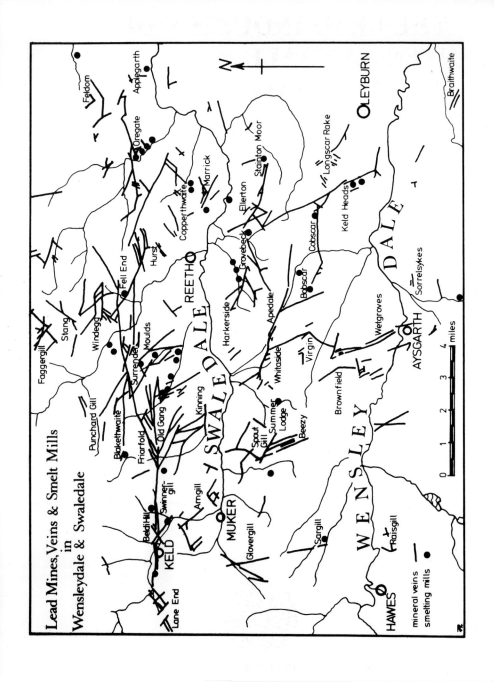

Lead Mines, Veins & Smelt Mills
in
Wensleydale & Swaledale

mineral veins ——
smelting mills ●

0 1 2 3 4 miles

Feldom
Applegarth
Oregate
Marrick
Stainton Moor
Longscar Rake
Copperthwaite
Ellerton
Keld Heads
Fell End
Hurst
Grovebeck
Cobscar
Braithwaite
OLEYBURN
REETH
Stang
Windegg
Moulds
Harkerside
Apedale
Babscar
Wetgroves
Sorrelsykes
Faggergill
Punchard Gill
Surrender
Kinning
Whitaside
Virgin
Brownfield
AYSGARTH
Blakethwaite
Friarfold
Old Gang
Spout Gill
Summer Lodge
Beezy
Swinner-gill
Arngill
SWALEDALE
WENSLEY
DALE
Bedd Hill
KELD
MUKER
Glovergill
Sargill
Raisgill
HAWES
Lane End

THE LEAD INDUSTRY OF WENSLEYDALE AND SWALEDALE

Vol 1
The Mines

Arthur Raistrick

MOORLAND PUBLISHING COMPANY

ISBN 0 86190 185 1

© A. Raistrick 1975
Paperback edition 1991

COPYRIGHT NOTICE
All rights reserved. No part of this publication may be
reproduced, stored in a retrieval system, or transmitted ,
in any form or by any means, electronic, mechanical,
photocopying, recording or otherwise, without the prior
permission of Moorland Publishing Company Ltd.

Printed in the UK by
The Cromwell Press Ltd
Broughton Gifford, Wiltshire

For the Publishers:
Moorland Publishing Co Ltd
Moor Farm Road, Ashbourne, Derbyshire, DE6 1HD

Contents

Illustrations

Maps

Grateful acknowledgment is made to L. J. Barker, A. Butterfield, H. M. Parker, and B. Unne for the use of photographs in this book. Illustrations not otherwise acknowledged are from the author's own collection.

INTRODUCTION

Nearly twenty years ago the book *Mines and Miners of Swaledale* was published, but it has long been out of print. During the twenty years much new material relating to the lead mines of Yorkshire has come to light and this, with continued field work, has made a new and extended edition of this book possible. An important mass of new knowledge became available a few years ago with the discovery of the large collection of more than 3,000 manuscripts belonging to Philip Swale, the agent and friend of Philip 4th Lord Wharton in the second half of the seventeenth century. Studies already made on a collection of manuscripts of Philip Swale which were lodged in the Library of the Society of Friends in London were extended when that collection was transferred to the North Yorkshire County Record Office at Northallerton and added to the new finds. These are now listed under the title *MSS of Richmond Monthly Meeting of the Society of Friends (RQR)*. A search of the vast mass of other contemporary manuscripts, now calendared by the Records Office staff soon made a revision of our ideas of the early mining history necessary. Many of the results of this work are included in this book and some are finding their place in an extended study of Philip Swale and Philip Wharton.

During the last ten years this research has led to a revision of all previous work on the smelt mills and their history. The preparation of the *History of Lead Mining in the Pennines* (Longmans 1965) in which Bernard Jennings collaborated, necessitated a review and revision of all previous work on that area. The nett effect is that a fuller and clearer account of the history of many of the mines can now be given than was the case in 1955. In view of the new material available it seems logical to extend the story by including the Wensleydale and Stainmore mines. The opportunity is also taken to add a chapter on the long history of coal mining in the area, partly because its remains are frequently confused with those of the lead mines, and partly because there is no easily available account of this industry, which at many points was closely linked with the smelting side of the lead industry. A brief notice is also given to the occasional occurrence of copper ores and the attempts which have been made to establish copper mines.

Many people have helped to make this reassessment of the mining field possible. The North Riding County (now North Yorkshire County) Record Office through Mr M. Y. Ashcroft, the County Archivist, has allowed the use of material gathered from the documents in his keeping. David Hall, a member of his staff, has helped by drawing my attention to documents and discussing their relevance to my researches. I have been helped with transport and accompanied in much of my field work by my friends Norman Crossley and Lawrence J. Barker, by Mrs J. Harrison and Mrs. C. Hall (students and friends from my University Tutorial classes), and by David Hall. I benefited by many discussions with my late friend John Rowntree whose discovery and preservation of the Philp Swale manuscripts opened up the new chapter in the study of Swaledale mining and of the early history of the Quakers in Swaledale and Wensleydale. Through such generous help and interest it has been possible to revisit the whole of the mining field and re-examine all the mines and their remains. This in one way has been the cause of much disappointment at the rapid deterioration and even destruction of monuments during the last few years. It is hoped that perhaps a few of the remaining buildings can still be preserved. The vandalism for no apparent reason at such places as the Blakethwaite and Old Gang Smelt Mills is depressing in the extreme.

Chapter 1

THE OCCURENCE OF ORES AND COAL

The mining field with which this book deals is approximately Swaledale with Arkengarthdale, part of Wensleydale and some of the Greta drainage. This area is almost entirely formed of rocks of the Carboniferous system, belonging mainly to the Yoredale Series and to the Millstone Grit, with a small area of Permian Magnesian Limestone on its eastern edge. The Yoredales are a group of strata in which limestones, shales and sandstones follow one another in a repeated and regular order, while above them the sandstones of the Millstone Grit form the summits of many of the fells. The Yoredale series of rocks total more than a thousand feet thickness. The rocks of most importance to the miner are the limestones and a few of the sandstones and these have names by which they are known over all the district. In order from bottom upwards the principal limestones are the Hardraw, Simonstone, Middle, Five Yards, Three Yards, Undersett and Main and these are separated by shales and sandstones of varying thickness. Above them are the Chert Beds, the Ten Fathom Grit and then Crow and Fell Top limestones.

This great thickness of strata is broken by numerous faults along which there has been vertical fracture and displacement varying from very little to as much as several hundred feet. Along some of these faults, in which various minerals including the ores of lead have been deposited to form the veins, the mining has taken place. Coal seams which occur under some of the limestones and in the base of the Millstone Grit are normal sediments and they lie in and parallel to the strata in strong contrast to the mineral veins which cut almost vertically through them. At a period in the earth's history before the Carboniferous, there was a major intrusion of molten rock magma from very great depth. This was of granitic composition and it reached up to near the base of the Carboniferous rocks. In fact a portion of such a granite mass has been found recently (1973) in a deep borehole in Raydale, south of Semerwater. As the magma cooled and after the Carboniferous strata had been faulted,

sulphides and other compounds of lead, copper and zinc, with some
of barium and fluorine, were squeezed out of the magma in solution,
and it was this mineralising solution which found escape through
many of the faults. In these cooler parts minerals were deposited by
crystalisation and some by reaction of the solution with favourable
limestones, so forming the mineral veins.

The chief ore of lead, galena (lead sulphide), was accompanied by
other minerals, calcite (calcium carbonate), baryte (barium
sulphate), witherite (barium carbonate) and fluorite (calcium
fluoride) with in some parts small quantities of copper minerals and
traces of zinc minerals. Of these minerals galena is the ore from
which metallic lead is got by smelting, and the others are called
gangue minerals. The strings of ore may be only a few inches thick
and so to have work room the miner has often to excavate gangue
minerals as well as rock and these were left on the tips.

The mineral filling of a vein is by no means regular either in depth
or in lateral extent. In fact the ore is usually present only for a
limited extent, forming an ore shoot. These are found more
commonly in the faults where displacement is not very great and
where the rocks between the Undersett Limestone and the Ten
Fathom Grit are still close together across the fault and forming its
cheeks. The richest ore shoots seem to have formed in faults of only a
few fathoms throw (a fathom is two yards). The vein filling depends
on so many different factors that there can be no regularity about it,
hence the highly speculative character of mining. A likely fault may
contain an excellent ore shoot of many fathoms extent, both vertical
and horizontal; the ore shoot may be fairly regular or it may swell
out into a large mass. Also it may fairly quickly nip out or thin to
almost nothing, and the fault or vein may contain only gangue
minerals or be devoid even of these. In such cases the miner must
continue working along the fault or barren vein until another ore
shoot comes in. It is never possible to predict when or if this will
happen and there are many cases of a company or a group of men
spending all their resources following a barren vein then giving up
not long before another and sometimes rich shoot comes in. These
facts have provoked innumerable legends about ore just beyond
where the mine left off, and account for the willingness of the miner
to continue to press forward in never failing hope.

Besides the vein with an ore shoot, ore is occasionally deposited in another kind of mass, as flats, sometimes called floats. These are lateral deposits where the mineralising solution has penetrated sideways between limestone beds, sometimes into small caverns to make flat cakes, fillings or lenticles of ore. These are the richest kind of deposit, often being of ore with very little gangue. They occurred in the veins on the south side of Swaledale and particularly in Spout Gill, Whitaside, Grovebeck and Grinton Moor, associated with veins of very small throw. The southern fringe of the field in Wensleydale is particularly marked by the occurrence of small flatting deposits. There is a strong contrast between the vein deposits such as the great Friarfold complex in Swaledale with its long succession of good ore shoots for ten miles or more and the area in Wensleydale. As will be seen from the mine descriptions, the few large mines there are on the southern prolongation of veins branching from Swaledale east-west veins. There is a large number of scattered small shafts and mines, particularly those south of the river, on very short veins which would never have been successful had it not been for the occurrence of numerous small flats. Most of the mines are small trials not worth recording separately but a few have been lucky in striking a flat which could not have been predicted, but being found had made a profitable mine for a few years.

The vertical extent of the mineralised zone is not very great, the majority of veins being most productive in the Main Limestone and Chert Beds which come above it. Where vein faults are of less than five fathoms throw they generally bear well in the Undersett Limestone below the Main. As the valleys cut through these limestones and the valley floor is generally well below the Undersett, most of the mining is on the higher ground. The top of the main production zone is seen near the Ten Fathom Grit which lies just below the base of the Millstone Grit on most of the moors.

Veins abound on the hillsides on both sides of the Swale valley but are particularly strong and numerous on the northern side between Keld and Marske. The bulk of the veins run in a direction either approximately east to west or north-west to south-east and some of the largest are in a belt roughly parallel to the valley about a mile or so north of the river. These veins are cut across by the Arkengarthdale valley and the tributaries of the Swale and were exposed on some of the hillsides and so were soon discovered and worked. On the south side of the valley the veins are principally north-west to south-east, branching from the east-west group and crossing the watershed into Wensleydale. It is the strongest of these which are worked around Grinton, in Apedale and around Wensley.

The great zone of veins which stretches from near Loanin End west of Keld extends eastwards to Arkengarthdale and continues east for a few miles through the Fell End mines and Hurst, but north of Marrick begins to thin out and east of Marske Beck there are only a few small and widely scattered veins.

Except for a few small mines and trials the mining area can be taken to end in Marske township north of the river. To the south there are mines along a small group of east-west veins to the east of Grinton, taking the mining area as far as Stainton Moor, with small trials at Downham and Hudswell Moor. Small mines are scattered in many parts of Wensleydale, particularly between Askrigg and Leyburn, but the only large scale mining was in Apedale near Bolton Castle and at Keld Heads near Wensley. The mines south of the river were mostly small and not very numerous.

To complete the picture for the North Yorkshire dales, a brief mention can be made of two areas in the drainage of the Tees. On Scargill Moor just west of Spanham a group of small veins was discovered and worked by Lord Scrope of Danby in 1711. Two years later mines in Ellergill were added with a lease for 21 years though it is not clear that these mines worked for more than a very few years.

The mineral field of the Dales is separated from that of Alston Moor, the southern part of which reaches into Teesdale, by a big geological feature, the downfold of the Stainmore Syncline. The northern flank of this fold is traversed by a dislocation of the strata, the Lunedale Fault, and along this there is a group of mines which are in North Yorkshire and so might have a brief mention for completeness. The fault runs eastward from near Brough under Stainmore to near Middleton in Teesdale and cuts the spurs of the hills on the north side of Lunedale and is mineralised near Closehouse, across the Arngill valley and to the hill of Standards. On all this part there are some very old hushes which reveal a massive deposit of baryte as well as of lead ore. The southern veins of the group were leased and worked from 1770 to 1880 by the London Lead Company and were very productive during the nineteenth century when the whole group of eight east-north-east veins was opened out as the Lunehead Mines, the ore being taken to the Egglestone Mills in Teesdale for smelting. In 1884 the mines were re-opened for baryte and became one of the largest producers in the country and are still worked as the Closehouse Mines.

On the eastern edge of the Dales the Yoredale series and Millstone Grit strata are covered by the Magnesian Limestone of Permian age and in this rock, to the north and east of Richmond, there are a few isolated deposits of copper ores. At Middleton Tyas the copper deposits were of sufficient size to support some large mines and a smelt mill for nearly half a century. The ore was not in veins like the lead ores, but was in irregular areas of impregnation or part-replacement of the limestone by ores of copper. Small impregnations, but of no commercial value are found in many parts of the Magnesian Limestone.

Besides these there was a proportion of copper ore, sufficient to be worked, in part of a big lead vein which crosses Feldom Moor and which for a time kept the Copper Mill near Washton in work. Several small veins in the Carboniferous strata, all very short, between this and the Middleton deposits carried copper ores and some were known as early as the sixteenth century. Other copper deposits were found on the western edge of our mineral field just within the dales area and along the Westmorland border. These were exceptional, with small veins around Dent and in Mallerstang, and although they were tried they never formed a successful mine.

In addition to the lead and copper minerals, a little iron ore has been worked, mainly for mediaeval iron bloomeries, but it has never been more than a small and very local effort. In strong contrast to this is the very widespread mining of coal which has left traces in all parts of the Dales, some of them of far greater extent than anything left by mining lead. The coal seams are entirely different in formation and mode of occurrence from the mineral veins, as they were not intruded into the rocks, but are a normal part of the succession of strata deposited in and around the Carboniferous seas. The Yoredale series of rocks was formed in a shallow sea which from time to time became so shallow as to form extensive estuarine swamps where forests could grow. Subsidence followed these periods and the debris of the forests which had accumulated as peat was submerged and covered with limestone or shale muds and eventually formed coal. There are workable coal seams below the Undersett,

Main and Little Limestones with very poor quality seams below the Middle Limestone. These coals are very variable in thickness and quality over all the area and have been mined extensively only where they are thickest or suitable for some special purpose. The coal below the Middle Limestone contains a lot of ash and sulphur which makes it unsuited for domestic use, but it is good enough for lime burning. Hence there is an abundance of small pits which are sunk or driven on this coal near limekilns over a great part of the lower hill slopes, particularly in Wensleydale.

Besides the Yoredale coals there is a good coal, sometimes in two seams, in the lower part of the Millstone Grit and this is the Tan Hill Coal, worked extensively for many centuries on the higher fells around Tan Hill and the Westmorland border.

As the coals occur in horizontal seams, where they are not too deep they have been worked by bell pits and many collieries are marked by a great spread of close-set pits, even on some collieries, like those of Preston Moor between Leyburn and Grinton, numbering a few hundreds. The only way of differentiating a small group or isolated pit from that of a lead trial, is by examining the material of the heap. In a coal pit the tip is always of shale, free from spars and stone, and often fragments of coal will be found in the debris.

Chapter 2

THE EARLY PERIOD OF MINING

For some time before the coming of the Romans, the Dales had been part of the kingdom of Brigantia, and the Brigantes — the Iron Age confederation of tribes which occupied much of the North Pennines — were skilled metal workers. Many of their dwellings have been excavated and small articles made of lead, fragments of smelted lead and occasional bits of ore have been found among them. Most of these metal objects found in huts are of Romano-British age, but a few in pre-Roman settlements and some other evidence suggests that some ore was possibly collected at surface outcrops or gathered from stream gravels, and some of this was smelted before the Romans came.

It is known that after the defeat of the Brigantes by the Roman forces under Petilius Cerialis at the great fort of Stanwick just north of Richmond, in the year AD74, some of the prisoners taken by the Romans were used as slave labour in mines at Hurst and Greenhow. This would be in accord with common Roman practice in other parts of the country and on the Continent. It is most likely that the Romans took over and developed mines already discovered and opened by the natives. At the Hurst Mines about three miles from Marrick, a pig of smelted lead was discovered during the nineteenth century. Its cast-on inscription included the name of the Emperor Adrian and so was produced during his reign, AD 117-138. Unfortunately this pig cannot now be traced, probably having suffered the fairly common fate of being melted down for plumbers' lead. The mines and the little hamlet of Hurst must therefore have been a penal settlement for a time and may later have gained a certain amount of freedom as the generation of prisoners died out. The lead it produced was probably sent to the Roman stations of Catterick and York.

We do not know how long the Hurst Mines continued to work. In fact for many centuries after the withdrawal of the Romans we have no evidence of mining which can point to any particular mine. Lead however was in demand by the Anglian settlers for use for coffins, pipes, tanks and in buildings. In 690 William of Malmesbury in his chronicle says of York Minster that it was half ruined, but 'the Bishop [St Wilfrid] moved by grief at this unworthy state of affairs, strengthened the masonry, raised the roof, and when it was raised protected it from injury by storms with leaden sheets.' This lead presumably came from the Yorkshire mines and could have been brought easily from Swaledale, down the river.

After the Norman Conquest the Honour of Richmond which included all Swaledale and Wensleydale became the property of Count Alan of Brittany who built Richmond Castle. In this there was a great demand for lead for pipes, cisterns, roofing and many other purposes in and about the buildings. Besides granting the working of lead mines to meet this demand — the mines being mainly in Count Alan's Arkengarthdale area — the monks of Jervaulx in 1145 received a grant of the right to dig and use lead and iron throughout the Count's forest of Wensleydale. The old mines must have been developed and some new ones discovered and opened to meet this new demand for lead, and by the end of the twelfth century they had progressed sufficiently to have lead to spare for export. Between 1179 and 1184 large quantities of lead (526 carretates or cartloads) were exported, some from Yarm and some from Boroughbridge. This was at the king's command, some of the lead being for roofing Waltham Abbey, some for Windsor Castle, and some was sent to Clairvaulx Abbey in France. It is likely that this lead was from the Crown lands in Swaledale.

At this period it is clear from the Pipe Rolls, the records in which the exports just mentioned are documented, that the mines of the Honour of Richmond were closely associated with those of Alston Moor, an association which lasted until 1223. The king had granted his protection to the miners of Alston Moor, along with many privileges which placed them in a fairly independent position, and in 1219 a Royal Mandate extended protection to the miners of Grinton giving them protection and restoring to them the conditions of work which they had enjoyed under Henry II. Grinton included all upper Swaledale and much of Arkengarthdale at that time and these were almost certainly the mines which had provided lead for Waltham and Windsor. There was a mine working in Arkengarthdale in 1285 which gave a profit of £4 (worth in present-day equivalent more than forty to fifty times as much). This may have been either Punchard Gill or Faggergill.

The mines are mentioned in documents in the fourteenth century in such a way as to show that they were being worked with some regularity. When money was being raised in 1307 for building the town wall of Richmond the king granted tolls on goods sold in Richmond market, and these included a toll of 2d on every cartload of lead. Unless lead was regularly sold there, the toll would not have had much value. Towards the end of the thirteenth century we first learn the names of some of the lead merchants, and their number is strong evidence of the importance of the industry. From Arkengarthdale were Alan Pagot, Roger Pagot, John de Ponford, Richard Blauer, Robert Pakot, Alan Gille and Thomas Fitz Ralph; from Redmire were Eudo and Laurence; and from Preston-under-Scar were Thomas Fitz Richard, John de Hauton and William de Cover. These were not necessarily merchants in the fullest sense of the word, but were more likely to be actual miners bringing their lead into the markets. Lead was sold in the markets at Richmond, Barnard Castle and Kirkby Malzeard and some was supplied direct to Richmond Castle and some to Jervaulx Abbey. The trade was expanding and new mines were opened from time to time. One new mine was at Downham for instance, in 1396.

There are many scraps of evidence to show that mines were being worked in Arkengarthdale and around Grinton throughout the Middle Ages, but there is no direct evidence to show that the monks of Jervaulx and of Rievaulx worked mines in their areas of upper Wensleydale and Swaledale. It would not be unreasonable, however, to expect that they would, like other Cistercian communities, work ores of lead where they could to meet their own requirements, or even to trade as did Fountains Abbey.

The Manor of Grinton in part had been granted to Bridlington Priory in 1312 and at the dissolution in 1538 this reverted to the Crown. About twenty years later the mines within this part of the Manor were leased to Henry Lord Scrope and Arthur Phillipe for a yearly rent of twenty shillings along with the mines of Fremington for a similar amount. By the middle of the sixteenth century mines were being worked in Arkengarthdale, in New Forest, in Healaugh, Grinton, Marske and in parts of Wensleydale.

The whole question of leasing mines was in somewhat of a

confused state and the seeds of many future disputes and quarrels were sown by granting large over-riding concessions at a time when individual ownership was beginning to be recognised. In 1504 Christopher Conyers of Marske left by will 'halfe a more mere' (or lease of part of a vein) in 'Whitnowsyke in the workynge of James Atkynson and halfe anothere more mere there in the workynge of Edmund Tod.' He also left to his son a 'more mere' which he had bought of Thomas Metcalfe. His son in 1521 obtained a regrant of all his lead mines for 40 years at a rent of 63s 4d a year and in 1531 left his mines in Punchard Gill to his heir by will. In 1533 Henry VIII granted to Sir James Metcalfe all mines in the Lordships of Middleham and Richmond, 'parcels of lands assigned for the payment of the Captain, officers and soldiers of Berwick, except the said mines' which had been leased to Conyers. No other mines were thus excepted and in the seventeenth century there was an unhealthy crop of disputes and legal troubles arising from such a sweeping grant.

A further cause of trouble was the unsatisfactory definition of boundaries. Grants from the Crown were regularly made in terms of Lordships, Manors, wastes and commons, at a time when few of these has been marked out on the ground or decided by law. The wastes had little interest except for the game upon them, and wastes ran together without boundaries on the high and remote fells. The granting of leases of manors or of the wastes of a manor led to much searching for good definitions, to much riding of boundaries, fixing of lines and landmarks, and argument on the border lands. It was not until new and more precise methods of leasing were adopted that lawsuits became fewer in number and mining was relieved of a heavy burden of uncertainty.

The sixteenth century saw the rise of the York merchants who sent their purchased lead to Hull for shipping abroad or to London. There were many disputes and much grumbling that Hull merchants were levying unjust dues and charges, so about 1530 lead was taken to be weighed and marked at the common crane in York. The York merchants, however, were not above turning a dishonest penny at the expense of the miners, and a petition from the lead miners of Yorkshire to the king states that although the king had had sets of standard weights cast in brass and copies of these sent to all the county towns, and that there was a set of these weights in the

Guildhall at York, the merchants continued to use their own weights. These were heavier than the standard by as much as thirty or forty pounds in each five hundredweight. Furthermore the merchants insisted on placing in the scale an extra weight of seven pounds when each great piece of lead was weighed. In this way the miners were steadily robbed and the merchants grew rich. These exactions along with the tolls and charges for weighing, storing and shipping the lead were more than the miners cared to tolerate.

In the second half of the sixteenth and the early part of the seventeenth centuries the mines had a period of prosperity and expansion as the demand for lead in new houses and buildings rapidly increased. The returns of lead produced and the rents paid for the mines increased as well. This was also a period of fairly rapid change in the methods of working and smelting lead ore. The earliest mining had been confined to very shallow work on a few veins that were fairly rich at the surface. It is certain that a method called hushing was used from the earliest times, mainly for the discovery of veins. This method was used when a steep hillside was to be explored. On the crest of the hill a spot was chosen where a sod dam could be made to impound some of the drainage. At the right moment the dam was broken and a torrent of water, like a cloud-burst in force, tore down the slope cutting a trench through the soil and subsoil, often digging out the looser weathered rock to some depth. The debris spread out at the foot of the hill where the miner could easily sort it over. If veins of ore were present in the hillside they would be shown in the trench and also a quantity of ore torn from them could be collected from the gravels. This method was widely used until late into the nineteenth century, so that now, although hushes can be seen in all parts of the mining areas, it is not easy to point to any one and say with certainty that it is a very ancient one.

When veins had been discovered they were generally worked by digging a trench along them, making an open cut. Bell pits are shallow shafts, now seen as funnel-shaped hollows surrounded by a ring of debris, and they often occur in numbers spreading in a row along the run of a vein. The miners sunk such a shaft on the vein to a depth possibly of twenty feet or more, and then worked out laterally along the vein from the sides. As they had no special provision for ventilation such work could not extend far before the air got foul. so

another shaft was sunk nearby along the vein and the earlier one
abandoned, possibly receiving some debris from the second. The net
result is a line of bell pits spaced out along a vein like loosely strung
beads. The ore was broken out with pick and hammer and, during
the later part of the period at least, with gads and plug-and-feathers.
The gad is a sharp-pointed iron wedge, and the feathers are two flat
pieces of iron of the same width as a long wedge, called the plug.
Gads were used to drive into cracks or to start holes which could be
deepened with a pick point or drill to hold two feathers. The plug
could then be driven between the feathers with a heavy hammer.
With two or three sets of wedges placed closely and wisely the rock
was soon burst out. Plugs and feathers were the general method
used in mining before the introduction of gunpowder and they have
been found in many older workings.

   The mixed ore, gangue and stone taken from the mine, called
bouse, was crushed and then washed with running water in a stream
just strong enough to carry away the lighter stone and dirt and to

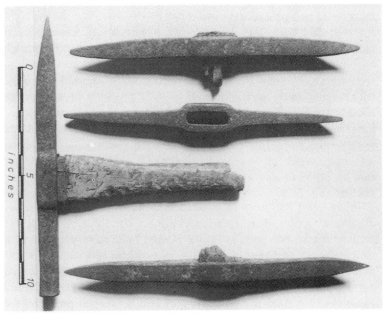

Miners' picks from the Wensleydale mines.

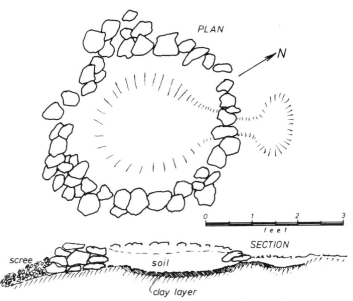

Bail hill for smelting lead at Winterings, Gunnerside.
above: plan and section of the site, as measured in 1919.
below: reconstruction showing the arrangement for smelting.

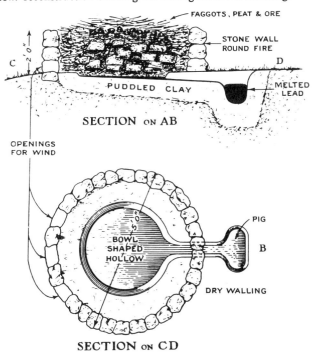

SECTION ON CD

23

leave the heavy ore. The finely crushed ore, or smitham, was reserved
for smelting. The oldest method of smelting was that of the bail hill.
The bail hill site was chosen on a low hill, often facing south-west,
the direction of the prevailing wind. A small space, a few feet in
diameter was surrounded by a low wall of stones with openings
towards the windy quarter; the loose soil was scooped out into a
hollow and often lined with clay, with a run-off channel leading
outside the walled space. A layer of brushwood and peat was built up
inside and when a steady fire was burning, the crushed ore was
sprinkled on top. With a steady draught and the constant addition
of wood and peat a temperature sufficient to oxidise the ore could be
got. Ore was fed from time to time and as a bed of red hot charcoal
built up and the oxidised ore and some galena dropped down into it,
the oxide was reduced and lead began to flow out through the
channel into a hole made to receive it. It could cool in this into an
irregular lump or be scooped into more regular clay moulds. Many
bail hills with the characteristic position and old slags around them
are to be found in Swaledale and Wensleydale, mainly along the hill
edges.

Chapter 3

SIXTEENTH AND SEVENTEENTH CENTURY EXPANSION

The second half of the sixteenth century saw what almost amounted to a revolution in mining methods. The Elizabethan period was a time of prosperity with a greatly increased demand for metals, particularly copper and lead, and many things were done to encourage the mining industry. Miners were brought from Germany to develop the copper mines of the Lake District in 1564, and they brought with them new mining tools and methods that had just then been fully described and illustrated in Agricola's great work *De Re Metallica* published in 1556. (See Bibliography).

The Germans at the copper mines at Newlands near Keswick were sinking deeper shafts, using water wheels, pumps and other machinery and smelting their ores in a form of blast furnace in which they even experimented with coal as a fuel. They were not, however, the only people to be experimenting with improvements — miners in Durham and in Derbyshire already had used bail hills with foot bellows for a better draught, and new types of furnace were being tried. One method used by the Germans was that of driving a level, or nearly horizontal tunnel, into the hillsides to reach a vein, in preference to sinking a very deep shaft. This had many advantages and contributed to solving one difficulty that was troubling the miners more and more. As shafts were sunk by the old method, with many abandoned shafts along a vein, water accumulated which often interfered with working shafts, and also became a dangerous menace as it stood in the old workings. An adit to drain water from a mine had been made in this country as early as 1302, at Bere Alston, Devon; at Baxenden in Rossendale, Lancashire, in 1304-5, miners were paid 'for making a certain trench underground to draw off from the other trenches.' The use of levels to approach a mine however, was brought into common use by the Germans and spread slowly over the northern fields, and water was got rid of from many

25

An early hand-cut level, driven in the days before gunpowder was widely used.

mines by the old method of lifting up the shaft in buckets, until quite late. An adit had the advantage of draining a large area of ground above its level, but the expense of driving was only to be borne by a large company.

In 1552 Burchard Kranich in Derbyshire had made a furnace for smelting lead ores and in 1565 William Humphray patented a furnace which had most of the characteristics of what became the 'ore hearth' the most widely used type of furnace in the next few centuries. The earliest smelt mill we know in Yorkshire was the one at Clints near Marske, which was sold in 1589 with two furnaces. New methods of preparing the ore for the ore hearth included washing on sieves, a method also due to Humphray and Burchard. In the new method of dressing the ore needed to be crushed to a smaller size and the washing was designed to get rid of all the stone and spar that was mixed in the house. The crushing was done by hand using a bucker, a flat hammer of iron and was largely the work of girls and boys. The crushed ore was carried to the sieves.

The principle of ore dressing lies in the greatly differing densities of lead ore and the stone and spars which occur with it. If all are crushed to the same small size and the mixture is stirred in water and then allowed to settle, the ore will tend to settle first and the stone a little later, giving a partial separation with a concentration of ore at the bottom of the settled bouse. A stream of water may be arranged with a velocity which is strong enough to carry off the stone but not sufficient to move the ore. This use of a stream is called buddling and ore dressing in the sixteenth and seventeenth centuries was mainly by hand crushing, picking, sieving and buddling, and these remain the basic principles of later mechanised methods.

As dressing developed it settled into a regular pattern and the remains on a dressing floor are easily recognised. Bouse from the mine was placed in some form of hopper, bouse team or bing stead from the bottom or front of which it could be raked forward onto a knock stone where it was broken with a bucker and hand picked. The broken stuff could be raked over a grate in a stream of water from which small ore and stone was washed down a trough or launder, either stone or wood, into a pit or trunking box, ready for the next process. Ore lumps too big to go through the grate were hand picked and put into the bing stead where ore for the smelt mill was stored. The sludge from the trunking box was next taken to the hand sieves where a shovelfull, put onto a sieve by a girl server, was shaken in a tub of water using a strong and repeated downward jerking movement. On all the mines of Lord Wharton in Swaledale in the late seventeenth century, this was done by women who worked in small partnerships and many employed their daughters as servers. In this shaking the bouse was lifted in the rush of water through the sieve mesh, then settled roughly in layers with ore at the bottom and stone at the top. Between these two distinct layers there was a mixed layer called chats. The stone could be scraped off the top and returned to be crushed to sand with the bucker, for a repeated sieving. The ore layer is put to the next process. Ore being very brittle there is a considerable amount which goes through the sieve and accumulates in the bottom of the tub and may form a fairly pure layer of smitham which can go to the smelt mill. With the many

streams of water used in dressing some quantity of very fine ore
tends to be carried away, so the water is run into settling pits or slime
pits where sludge settled out, containing a recoverable amount of
ore. This sludge and fine ore is treated in the buddle.

The buddle in its simplest form is a wide box or a wooden launder,
perhaps a yard wide and two yards long, and slighlty inclined. A
constant and even stream of water flows through it. The slime is
slowly shovelled into the stream and the lighter stone dust is carried
away leaving ore and some stone on the top end. Here a boy with a
rake keeps it slowly moving across the stream to give it a chance for
complete washing. On some of the older mines the remains of such a
trunk buddle can be recognised. In the eighteenth century however
improved forms of buddles were introduced and their remains are
far more common.

It is clear that the first necessity for dressing was a constant
stream of water, and the old miners spent a vast amount of energy to
secure their water supply. All the hillsides and moor tops are
traversed by small water courses which often collect an almost

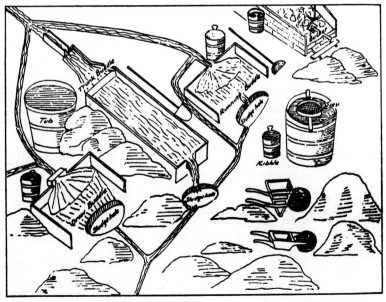

Diagram of an ore dressing floor. (Based on a drawing of 1808, *Mulcaster MS, Wigan Central Library).*

insignificant trickle of water to carry it round hill shoulders and across minor valleys to some small dressing floor, now hardly to be recognised except by the thin vegetation growing over the spread of tailings or reject sand and stone. As the mines grew in size the use of water sources became a lively subject of quarrel and dispute. As more was demanded dams were built and schemes put into operation that often resemble a sizeable water works.

As the mines increased in importance rival claims were made for them and out of some of these claims arose the expensive lawsuits of the seventeenth and eighteenth centuries. An early one of these concerns the Grinton mines and the family of Sir Solomon Swale of Swale Hall in West Grinton. The Swales were an ancient family and it claimed that one of them had built the north aisle of Grinton church, in a window of which was displayed the arms of the family. The manor of East Grinton containing the parish church had been given by Walter de Gaunt to Bridlington Priory about 1135, and at the same time West Grinton including Reeth, it is claimed, was given to Alured de Swale, nephew and chamberlain of Walter de Gaunt. Sir Solomon Swale claimed to be the descendant of Alured and through this said that he was the right owner of the mines and privileges of West Grinton.

In 1692 he gave a lease of part of Harkerside in West Grinton with its lead mines for thirty years to Philip Bickerstaffe of Newcastle and Charles Middleton of London, to work the mines at a royalty of one tenth. Five years later Sir Solomon claimed the manorial rights of all Grinton and started mining on Grinton Moor. The auditor of the Exchequer, one Hugh Marriot discovered that Grinton had been a 'concealed' manor for many years, not paying dues or rents to the Crown since the Restoration. In the name of 'Tushingham' he therefore applied for and obtained a Crown lease for twenty-one years of all the mines in Grinton and Harkerside at the old yearly rent of 20s. He started work on them and served a notice of ejectment on Sir Solomon Swale and all his workmen. This was disputed and a case was carried to trial at the bar. Sir Solomon Swale's claim was defeated.

Marriot was not left in undisputed possession for long. In 1707 Lord Wharton claimed the area in which Marriott was working (Harkerside) as part of the manor of Healaugh and forbade Marriot's men to do any more work unless they transferred to his employment. He sunk a new shaft on Grinton How near the one where Marriot was at work, and opened out a mine. Again the matter went to trial and a commission was appointed to investigate, which firmly established that Harkerside and Grinton were in fact part of the manor of Grinton.

The confusion over leases arose in part from the grants made to monasteries by the lords of the mediaeval Honours of Richmond and Middleham which covered much of Swaledale and Wensleydale. Very ill-defined grants had also been made to individuals about the time of the dissolution, such for instance as the grant of 'all mines in the Honours of Middleham and Richmond' already quoted. In 1605 a survey of the Honours was made which states that 'James Ward holdeth by lease for 14 years to come all the Cole and Lead Mynes within the lordshipp of Middleham paying yearly £4.0.0. By these formerly he received small benefitt but now nothing at all.' Then 'There are in the two Lordshipps Mynes of Cole and Lead in diverse places, but of small value.' And 'The mynes are taken of the King since the Cities contract by Humphrey Wharton, receyvor there.' In 1628 by Letters Patent the mines of Grinton and Fremington were leased to Humphrey Wharton and in the same year, 1628, a Roll in Chancery records that King Charles I granted the Lordships of Middleham and Richmond to Henry Ditchfield and Humphrey Clarke in recognition of a loan amounting to about £230,000 which they had advanced to him. The grant included Grinton and Harkerside and gave to them all profits of mines of lead and coal. Among many other things it mentions wayleaves 'to and from the said mines and whatever place or places lately in the tenure of Thomas Metcalfe, Knight, and now or late in the tenure and occupation of Humphrey Wharton.' In 1626 mines in Grinton and Fremington became the subject of controversy but after many changes Fremington was returned to Humphrey Wharton and were still in his family in the nineteenth century.

The mines in the Wharton estates were a more fortunate example. Thomas 3rd Lord Wharton in 1544 purchased the manor of Muker from the Crown and in 1556 added by purchase half the manor of Healaugh, which made a single estate from the boundary of Arkengarthdale to the head of the valley. By the end of the century mines were being worked on both manors, and in a dispute over Tenant Right holdings in Muker in 1618-19 we learn that Lord

Wharton had reserved to him for the use of his miners, all the timber on the commons of Muker, with the right to mine anywhere, to turn streams of water and to have right of access to and from any mines he may open. Thomas 3rd Lord Wharton had started working mines in Healaugh manor and when his grandson Philip inherited them in 1621 they appear to have continued to be worked, possibly under the care of Thomas Wharton, Philip's father and his agent Robert Swale. When Philip Swale in 1661 inherited his father's position as agent to Philip Lord Wharton, his papers show the mines along the Friarfold, Merryfield and Lownathwaite and some other veins to be very active. In leases and new partnerships made between Philip Lord Wharton, Philip Swale and Robert Barker, the leases are stated with a new precision, eg 800yd to the west from a stated point on the vein, and 100yd on each side of the vein. In this we can see the approach to the customary quarter cord of a width on each side of a vein, on which ground the miner could erect buildings, work, and tip debris. The Wharton accounts of working in the mines, on the washing floors and in the smelt mills, of carriage and sale of ore and lead, and even of the accommodation provided for the miners, from the 1660s are some of the earliest we have and they afford an accurate and remarkably detailed picture of life and work in many of the mines of Upper Swaledale.

The stimulus of prosperity led to a great exploration and search for new mines which resulted in many new trials being made throughout the area. Some of these became mines worked by small partnerships of miners, too small to have their own smelt mill, but finding a ready customer for their ore in such groups as the Whartons. The changes can perhaps be summarised in this way, that at the beginning of the seventeenth century Swaledale and Wensleydale had a few well-known mines, some of them very ancient, but by the end of that century they had become an area known to be rich in mineral veins with the possibility of many new mines to be opened. The time was ripe for a great expansion of the industry, with a new organisation of the mines and new techniques to be applied both to mining and smelting which were to lead into the period of greatest activity in the field.

Chapter 4

EIGHTEENTH CENTURY DEVELOPMENTS

The eighteenth century saw the opening of what might be called the modern period in lead mining. At the beginning of the century the great corporation of the London Lead Company (the Governor and Company for Smelting down Lead with Pit Coal and Sea Coal) had opened mines in North Wales and Alston Moor and had introduced the reverberatory furnace for smelting and better methods of refining lead. The mines of Derbyshire and of Wharfedale were being developed on a new scale, the steam engine was being applied to mine pumping and water wheels were being improved to drive machinery as well as for winding. In Swaledale the new period opened a little later, in the second quarter of the century, and the development of two fairly old mining sites in the upper valley can be used to illustrate some points in this story.

In Oxnup Gill, two miles south-west of Gunnerside, there are some very large hushes well seen from the Muker to Askrigg road from about High Oxnup. The main workings were by shafts at Spout Gill near the head of the hushes and on the high ground west of the gill. Spout Gill Mines had been leased by Lord Wharton to Alderman Thompson in 1682 and judging from an inventory of the tools there in 1715, which included 34 kibbles and 11 jack rollers with a large quantity of tools and dressing appliances, the mines were flourishing. In 1732 a report said that 'Spout Gill continues exceeding rich' and they 'are now more yn double in value wt was soe known in ye times of Ld. Phil or Ld. Thos' (Wharton). After the transfer of the Wharton estates to trustees they were sufficiently productive to attract the attention of the Company of Mine Adventurers who built a smelt mill in Foss Gill on the west side of Oxnup Gill, where, although the buildings have long since disappeared, the position is marked by foundations and some slags, a long water course and a dam. This mill was of an improved pattern and is well documented with a drawing in the Egerton MSS in the British Museum, titled *The Draught of a Smelting Mill used by the*

Company of Mine Adventurers of England and others in Yorkshire 1735. This drawing gives a detailed plan of two ore hearths, each served by a pair of bellows operated by a single waterwheel. The plate also illustrates the structure of the hearths and the variety of tools used (see volume 2).

The hushes used in the seventeenth century were developed on a new scale by the adventurers for which work an increased amount of water was needed. For the hushes dams were built with a sluice so that water could be accumulated and released repeatedly, and in the course of the hush a deep pit with a grate over it was constructed. After the first hush miners loosened rock in the floor of the hush with picks and crow bars and a torrent of water was then sent down which swept the loosened stuff over the grate, trapping much of the ore that was being moved. In this method a group of hushes might be in use for over a century and could grow to an enormous size.

The water for this scheme was at first collected on Satron Moor and a little brought from Summer Lodge Tarn and Satron Tarn, but in 1775 there was a dispute about this water and the Spout Gill miners turned to the west side of the valley for water gathered on Oxnup Moor. This involved the building of a long water course running south to the head of the gill, crossing the stream on a launder and coming back across Miles Pasture to Spout Gill Head. It is said that the miners built this water course in their spare time and were given £10 for the first quart of water to be delivered by it. The money was paid and spent at once at Jenkin Gate near the Muker road, which at that time was a public house largely patronised by the miners and smelters.

Spout Gill Mine proved to be rich and it was said that in one year one of the shafts raised £40,000 worth of ore. This, like many miners' traditions, might be exaggerated with time, but its existence is proof of a measure of richness. The greater part of the ore came from flats in the Great Limestone. In 1768 the shafts were fairly deep and, in order to reach a greater depth and also to deal with drainage, two levels were driven, one from Spout Gill and one from Stotter Gill, close by. These levels, however, were not of much profit as the veins proved to be thin in depth, and most of the production continued to come from the old shafts.

Until 1770 the Spout Gill Mill was kept busy smelting ore from Spout Gill Mines along with ore from two other groups of workings.

One was the Beezy Mines in Wensleydale, a series of small shafts near the boundary in the high ground east of the head of Oxnup Gill and the other the Beldi Hill Mines near Keld. The Spout Gill Mines and Mill continued to work until about 1870 but their greatest period was probably the latter half of the eighteenth century.

Near Keld the river Swale enters the spectacular Kisdon Gorge by Kisdon Force, then about a mile from Keld it turns south to Muker where it resumes its easterly course, having flowed around the north and east sides of Kisdon Hill. The north-south part of this course is almost a direct continuation of the south course of its tributary Swinnergill. A great east to west vein, part of the Friarfold complex, and here called the Cockrake, with a number of associated veins run eastward from Keld and they are cut by the head of Swinnergill where they have been worked at the Swinnergill Mines. On the hill between East Gill and Keld and Swinnergill there are the very old Beldi Hill Mines behind Crackpot Hall. The earliest workings were by hushes, one of which, the Old Field Hush, was developed and extended during the eighteenth century and was working as late as 1880.

Remains at Beldi Hill, Keld *(B. Unne).*

The Beldi Hill Mines were taken in 1742 by a local company made up of three brothers, John, Thomas and Ralph Parkes, and Leonard Hartley. While developing the Old Field Hush they also approached the veins by a level named Parkes Level, driven between 1746 and 1749 from the west side of Swinnergill, as drainage for the developing complex of veins. They got some amount of ore for a time, and carried it after dressing across the valley to Spout Gill Mill for smelting. From Parkes Level they worked to the west, while at the same time the veins to the east of Swinnergill were being worked from a number of shafts on behalf of Lord Pomfret. When the level was completed Lord Pomfret suggested that it might serve his mines which were on the eastward extension of the same veins, and Parkes & Company agreed to this. After a year however, Parkes found that the ground he was in was not very good and so decided to close the level. For some reason or other he walled it up, turned a stream from the moor into one of its shafts and flooded the level so flooding part of Lord Pomfret's mines. This act started a quarrel which was not settled and so in 1752 Pomfret began the Swinnergill Level from the east side of the beck to replace Parkes Level. Some time later Parkes drove another level, the Top Level into Beldi Hill and by 1770 this mine was sufficiently prosperous to justify the building of its own smelt mill, just at the mouth of Swinnergill at its junction with Kisdon. In 1769 Lord Pomfret built his mill in Swinnergill just where the main complex of veins crosses, and the remains of both mills can still be seen.

Beldi Hill Mines became the subject of a very tedious and expensive law suit which gave rise to many queer scenes and capers by the rival miners. To look back a few years, Lord Wharton had been attainted of treason after the 1715 rebellion, and in 1721 his estates which had been confiscated to the Crown were vested in trustees for the payments of his debts. The surplus income from the estates was to be used for the benefit of his two sisters Lady Jane Coke and Lady Lucy Morris. Lady Morris died some time after and left her portion of the estate income to her sister Jane Coke, who died in 1760. Her niece Anna Draycott inherited and in 1764 married George Fermor, 2nd Lord Pomfret. Their daughter Lady Charlotte, married Peter Denys, a London lead merchant, whose son George eventually inherited most of the mines, passing them on to his son, the well known and remembered Sir George Denys.

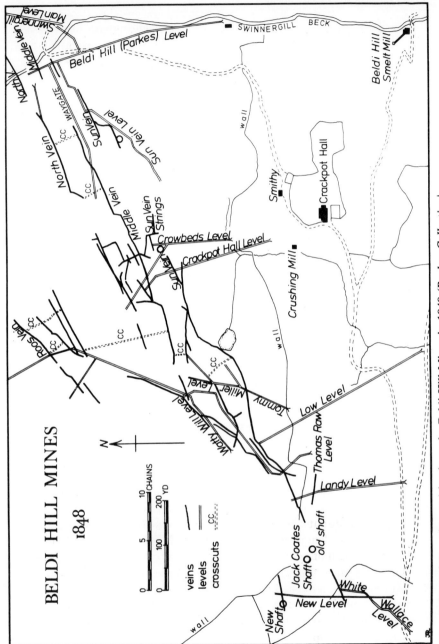

Map 1 Plan of the veins and levels at the Beldi Hill Mines in 1848 *(Barker Collection).*

In 1738 the manors of Muker and Healaugh were sold by the Wharton trustees to a Mr Thomas Smith for £10,500, but the mines and all mining rights in the wastes and commons were reserved to the trustees. The terms of this reservation were those found in most mining leases and a quotation of part of it will illustrate the scope of mining at this time. Where earlier leases had generally been confined to granting power to search for, dig and take away ore and to have the profits of mines in large and sometimes vague areas, the typical eighteenth-century leases defined all the stages and necessities of a mine. After reserving (or granting) all mines and mineral veins it gave

> full and free Liberty, Power, Privilege and Authority with Miners, Agents, Workmen and Labourers, to search for, dig, work, sink, make shafts, and use all other Ways and Means from Time to Time for finding discovering and working of such mines of Lead, Copper and Potters' Ore and Iron, and to make Drifts, Adits, Levels, and all other things necessary for the finding, raising and obtaining and getting the same, and also Dress and Cleanse the said Ore from Rubbish and Stone, and to erect any Engine or Engines upon the premises, and to turn or divert any Water or Waters, for the making of Water-courses and Dams, as shall be useful for the working of such Engines, or for other use or advantage of the said Works and Mines, or for Cleansing the said Ore, and also free liberty of Ingress, Egress and Regress, into and out of, and to make, have and use all convenient ways etc. . . . and to build and erect upon any part of the said Wastes convenient Houses or Cottages, for the Habitation of Agents, Workmen or Miners, whilst they shall be employed in and about the working such Mines, and raising of cleansing the said Ore and Minerals, and also . . . to build any Bingsteads, Smiths' Forges, Mills, Furnaces, Engines and Store Houses, Hovels, Buildings for Dressing, Bucking, Cleansing, Running down and Smelting, Refining and for putting up, Preserving and Keeping the said ore . . . also to Cut, Dig, Raise, etc. . . . all Peat, Turf and Turbary . . . as they may need for the mines, houses, smelting etc. . . .

This pictures almost all contingenies, and explains why and how there come to be so many small buildings scattered about on the mining area, quite outside the villages but near the mines. The lease of a mine specified a length along the vein and with it the quarter cord, which was a width of ground on each side of the vein, very variable from about 20yd to as much as 200yd, on which any or all of this building could be done, and rock rubbish and mine waste could be tipped. It also provided room for ore dressing. The engines mentioned in the above lease are mainly waterwheels and horse gins for lifting in the shafts.

Parkes and Company had taken their lease of Beldi Hill from Thomas Smith, as the owner of Crackpot Hall and its Out Pasture, paying to him a royalty on all the ore they got. The first step in the great dispute arose in 1767 when Parkes and Company sublet ten meers (300yd) of their ground in Hall Out Pasture, near the Old Hush, to Richard Metcalfe of Calvert Houses and John Scott of Reeth, with their partners. These subtenants were to pay their royalty to Smith but in addition, as subtenants were to pay forty shillings a fother on all the ores they got, to Parkes and Company. Their work was successful as they soon entered a rich vein and raised ore in the first two years which was valued at £2,026 16s 10d. Lord Pomfret, through his agent, claimed that the Hall Pasture was part of the wastes of the Manor of Muker reserved to him, and so all dues for the mines should be his and all leases got from him. Smith counterclaimed that the Hall Out Pasture had time out of mind been fenced from the waste and was part of Crackpot Hall Farm.

In July 1769 Lord Pomfret's men entered the ten meers of ground and to demonstrate ownership began to sink a shaft alongside one being worked by Metcalfe and Scott. An injunction was obtained pending trial of the issue, by which all money earned by Metcalfe and Scott was placed in the bank until judgement was given. The case went before a special jury at York, which included many experienced miners, and judgement was given for Smith and Parkes against Lord Pomfret. In 1772 Lord Pomfret again took the dispute, this time to the Court of Kings Bench at Westmister, but again lost his appeal. Appeal to the House of Lords, three times in two years, closed with the final verdict that the Crackpot Hall Estate was outside the wastes of the Manor and the mineral rights belonged to Smith. The expense of these many trials involved Lord Pomfret in debts for which he was imprisoned in the Tower of London.

While the trials were pending the miners carried on the quarrel. To assert his claim Lord Pomfret's agent, Mr. I'Anson, set miners to sink a shaft just east of the Hush, but on the next day Parke's men filled up what had been dug. Two more shafts were started only a few yards away but Parkes ordered the workmen off. I'Anson replied by giving Parkes a discharge in writing from working any of the mines on Hall Out Pasture. Metcalfe and others now seized possession of Spout Gill Smelt Mill to claim the Beldi Hill ore and lead which had been smelted and stored there, and to prevent Parkes from smelting any more. There was a fight but no-one was seriously hurt. Ore and lead was carried from the mill to Leyburn, a train of ten horses being used to take about 1,200 pieces, which would take several journeys. Mr Smith's agent now discharged Metcalfe from Spout Gill Mill and so the game swung back and forth. Metcalfe a little later 'by some extraordinary stratagem regained possession of Spout Gill Mill. No blood was shed upon this occasion.'

On Beldi Hill the miners of both parties were active and mischievous. 'While we were upon the field a number of men who were said to be workmen of the opposite party assembled together near to the Hush and Thomas Walker and another person (one of Metcalfe's servants) attempted to turn the water used for ore dressing down one of the shafts to water our men out, and Walker was very officious in doing it.' A few days later the water course to Smith's Raygill Mill in Old Gang Gill was cut and 'the damage would have been greater only they were hindered by a little Scotsman employed at the High Mill'. On Beldi Hill water was at last turned into a shaft 'and when David Brunskill tried to prevent this he was thrown into the Hush Gutter.'

When Lord Pomfret's men seized the ore at Spout Gill Mill, Scott and his partners feared that he might follow this by seizure on Beldi Hill, so about July 1769 they began to remove their ore from the mine and the smelt mill. Some 1,300 bings (about 520 tons) was taken to Crossgreen and Hartlakes and the remainder to Calvert Houses, where three small cowhouses were filled with ore. These cowhouses on Ivelet Side, near the boundary wall of Calvert House Farm, were then occupied by Scott's partner, Metcalfe, not to be confused with Pomfret's servant Metcalfe. The weight of the ore burst out the side walls of the cowhouses. They were never rebuilt but lie in ruins today, and bits of lead ore could at one time be found among them. Some of this ore was smelted at Grovebeck Mill in Grinton. The shafts sunk by Pomfret's men were completed and crosscuts were driven underground until at one point they broke through into Metcalfe's (Smith's servant) working and by violence all his miners were forced out.

After all the many years of trials and the calling of a very large number of witnesses, Smith's case was still upheld and the extent of Lord Pomfret's wastes and royalty were finally defined. This long protracted dispute indicates the value the miners placed upon their rights. The individual miners were not under any easy control and they made the dispute a very personal matter, playing tricks on each other, doing a certain amount of damage, and meeting each move by the other side with comparable counter moves. In the end Smith was awarded £400 compensation for the damage done by Pomfret's men. The chief benefit from the many trials was the very detailed exploration of mine law and custom, and clearer methods of determining and defining leases and ownership.

One change that was taking place at that time was in the methods of paying miners. Lord Pomfret in 1773 wrote strongly about certain abuses in the custom of working mines by 'bing tale', 'that is to say by so many Bings [8cwt] of Rough Ore before it is smelted, opening the door to the principal Agent and under-Agents to cheat, without a possibility of Detection.' For their friends and relations they might pay for partly dressed ore 'mixt with Dirt as if it was pure ore', while they made others do much more dressing before payment. They could also provide better and more timber for the shafts of their friends as well as giving other favours to some and not to others. Pomfret suggested that mines should be let at a duty paid in smelted lead, when all would pay alike.

On the technical side of mining the chief introductions in the eighteenth century were the greater use of levels driven in the valley side to some distance to intersect and give access to a vein, and the great improvements in ore-hearth smelting. It is not possible to say just which was the earliest level in the area, but as early as 1701 James Garton and partners at Lownathwaite were required to 'carry up the Levell wch is now or was lately begun in Lownathwaite gill'. An improvement in haulage that was made essential as the mines became deeper was the substitution of the whim or horse gin for the jack-roller for lifting ore or water from any great depth, because the weight of a long rope when unwound down the shaft soon became unmanageable. The horse gin or whim was only a roller or drum with its axle vertical, the bottom end rotating in a footstep bearing, the upper one in a supporting frame. Two horizontal arms allowed horses to be harnessed to it and by walking round a circular track they wound the rope on the barrel from which it was carried over pulleys at the shaft head.   The earliest certain reference is to the Whim Shaft on the Lownathwaite Mine, but in many of the accounts around that time there are items for timber and ironwork for

A horse gin for raising loads up vertical shafts. Although this etching by Sir Frank Short RA shows a gin at a Worcestershire colliery in 1883 it is typical of those used in most mining districts.

'engines' and there is no doubt that whims were in use by the end of the seventeenth century.

In 1742 the group of veins to the east of Swinnergill which had been opened by Lord Pomfret was leased by him to the London (Quaker) Lead Company, the lease being for the ground eastward to the forefield at Lownathwaite Level, and 800yd westward, 400yd in breadth to be held for 31 years. The company were to be free to follow all cross veins for 1,200yd and were to pay a royalty of one-seventh of all smelted lead. This was not the first entry of the London Lead Company into the dales. In 1733 they had proposed (Court Minutes, 31 August 1733) to purchase the manor and lease the mines of Grinton for £2,800. At the Court held on 5 September it was reported that the mines, manor and a smelt mill had been purchased for £2,625, being the mines of Whitaside, Harkerside and Grinton, bought from Hugh Marriott. In fact this was the purchase of the remaining 17 years of Marriot's Lease. In 1747 the same company obtained a lease from Mr Powlett for 31 years of the mines in the manor of Marrick, paying a one-eighth royalty. With their wide experience of mining in Wales, Derbyshire and all over the northern Pennines, the company was in a position to introduce better technical methods and in particular to develop the use of levels driven for access to the mines, and to make improvements in smelting practice.

In the eighteenth and the early part of the nineteenth century the changes which were made in smelting methods were very important. In principle the ore hearth was very simple, easy to construct and not expensive to run. The main part was the hearth, somewhat like a blacksmith's, built with large stones or in part with blocks of cast iron, having a rectangular cast iron box about two feet square and ten to fifteen inches deep. The bellows nozzle, or tuyer, entered at the back at the level of the top edge and in front of the hearth there was a shelf-like plate, the workstone, sloping slightly outward. Fuel and ore was supplied as judged by the smelter after a good fire had been started, and with the bellows blast the whole was soon brought to a temperature at which the ore began to 'sweat' with beads of molten lead dropping through the fire into the bottom of the hearth. Old cinders and lime could be added to help the process and the slag could be drawn off as the hearth filled with molten lead.

The process involved much working, during which lumps of ore and cinders, becoming pastey, were drawn onto the workstone and then pushed back into the fire where the heat was proper for the next stage. Fuel and ore could be added at intervals and the quantity of smelted lead increased until some could be drawn off by a groove in the workstone. This round of processes was repeated regularly in a shift and the melted lead was accumulated in a 'sumpter pot' which was kept heated. From this it could from time to time be ladled into cast-iron moulds and cast into pigs. The ore hearth was simple in operation and could quickly be got alight and heated for smelting and it could deal with small parcels of ore. It was thus the ideal furnace for small mines and partnerships and was the principal smelting furnace used all over the dales.

In the eighteenth century there was a great increase in the number and size of water wheels and the application of power to many of the ore dressing processes. One improvement was the Scotching, or hotching tub in which a sieve immersed in a tub of water as in the earlier dressing method, was hung from the end of a long lever and could be jerked up and down in the water much more efficiently, while the 'hotcher' could stand further away from the drenching splash of the water. By 1830 at the Grassington Mines in Wharfedale, Captain Barrett had supplied motion to the lever by linking it with a waterwheel, and this idea was rapidly adopted at many of the mines. The keive or Dolly tub was also introduced in the

A miner working a hotching tub at Faggergill Mines, about 1910.

late eighteenth century. In this a large tub of water (a 'dolly tub' was for long used in the Dales' houses, only displaced by the washing machine) was kept stirred while crushed bouse was scattered into it. When sufficient bouse was in it was allowed to settle and the settling and separation of the ore was helped by boys and girls who hammered rhythmically with a mallet on the side of the tub. Mechanical stirrers and hammers improved the operation of the keive considerably.

In the Alston Moor district power-driven rollers were used for ore crushing and about 1820 they were introduced in the Dales. Larger bellows at the smelt mills and more machinery on the dressing floors made heavy demands on water power, and this was met by enlarging old dams and by building many new ones to supply the increasing number of waterwheels. Many of these dams remain on the moors as tarns, Birkdale Tarn, Summer Lodge Tarn and Satron Tarn being among the early enlarged natural ponds. Many others were built like the Moss Dams on Ivelet Moor and Lownathwaite Moor, which played a very important part in the nineteenth century when the output of lead ore had increased beyond the quantities which could be dressed by hand methods. In the nineteenth century a few hydraulic engines were introduced underground where water carried down a shaft to them had sufficient head to operate quite powerful engines.

The nineteenth century was a period of a few large partnerships in which a number of local investors were interested and who, through a few companies leased, and worked large areas of ground. The Arkengarthdale and Derwent Company between 1800 and 1821 were working practically all the ground of Old Gang and Arkengarthdale. In 1821 this ground was leased by Jaques, Knowles, Tomlin and Company who in 1828 added the lease of the Old Gang which they worked until 1887. Tomlin and a Richmond surveyor, Bradley, formed the Blakethwaite Company, which from 1836 to 1867 developed the rich Blakethwaite Mines along with Lownathwaite and Swinngergill and built the fine mill at Blakethwaite. There are similarities of design about Blakethwaite and Swinnergill Mills which suggest that Swinnergill, a ruin in 1830, was rebuilt after that by the Blakethwaite Company. In 1873 this Company made a new partnership, the A.D. Company, to work the lower strata opened out by the Sir Francis Level. Robinson of Reeth and Chaytor of Spennythorne were now associated with Jaques, Knowles and Tomlin at the Old Gang and were also partners with Jaques in the Surrender Mines. Chaytor Rake in Wensleydale was the main source of the wealth of the Keld Heads Mines in which the Chaytor family held an important share.

There were a few other nineteenth-century companies such as the Keld Heads Company at Wensley and the Apedale Mining Company in Apedale who built some of the larger structures which are now valuable monuments to the past industry.

Chapter 5

DESCRIPTION OF THE MINES

The nineteenth century was the period of greatest activity in Swaledale and the mines were so numerous and extensive that only a few can be selected for mention in each group. It will be convenient to deal with the area in a few smaller districts and it will be possible to include a few incidents of a mine's history and also to add a little significance to the features most likely to be seen by the visitor.

Keld and the Dale Head

The remains of mines are neither very numerous nor very obvious in this area. There is no documentary evidence of mining before the eighteenth century but a lease granted in 1700 covered ground from Oxnup Gill to Keldside and in a document of 1715 mines were mentioned in Lover Gill on the edge of this area. By 1753 two mines were being opened at High and Low Birkdale, the latter being probably Lane End. Sleddale is a tributary to Birkdale (the westward continuation of Swaledale) and on the west side near the head there are two large hushes, Leaden Haw Gill and Hush Gutter. Where Sleddale joins Birkdale, in the junction of the two streams there is Lane End or Loanin End Mine. Between this and Keld there are several mine heaps and ruins near the river with Little Moor Foot Mine at Hoggarths, Keldside Mine at the junction of Whitsundale Beck with the Swale, and a third of a mile nearer to Keld the ruins of the smelt mill (now in part converted to agricultural buildings) on the south side of the river, and a few old levels. These mines were chiefly worked in the nineteenth century.

In 1825 a Mr Jaques took a lease of all the land west of Keld, including the old leased areas, and among other conditions had to erect an engine for pumping the mines to the west which were unworkable because of flooding. Fifty men were to be employed and this suggests a fairly large scale of working. A company was formed called the Little Moor Foot and Keldside Mining Company, which worked these mines until 1829, after which year they were leased in turn to Mr Jackson and then to Christopher Bradley of the

Blakethwaite Company. A second-hand 80hp steam engine bought
from Ashton Green Colliery was put on the Lane End Shaft in 1828
but was only used for ten years. The north shaft employed a
waterwheel for pumping but in spite of this with the steam engine
and another waterwheel, the mines were drowned out. The wheels
were driven by water from Birkdale Tarn which was altered from a
small natural tarn for this purpose.

A few levels were driven from the riverside. One is seen near
Smithy Holme Bridge, but they were not productive. In 1864 the
A.D. Company took the lease of all these mines and started to drive
the Sir George (Denys) Level from the side of Catrake Foss in Keld.
It was intended that this should drain all the Loanin End Mines, and
it was hoped that some new veins might be cut, but in 1868, after it
had been driven for 112 fathoms it was given up. The entrance is
romantically situated on the brink of the south end of the Catrake
Foss waterfall and can be approached by steps from the much higher
level of Keld village.

Beldi Hill and Swinnergill

These mines have already figured in our story but with little detail
of their situation. Leaving Keld by Keld Lane leads over the river
bridge at the foot of East Gill and across another bridge over East
Gill Beck. From that point a footpath and cart track lead past
Crackpot Hall on the northern rim of the Kisdon ravine, going to the
foot of Swinnergill then down the Swale side to Muker. Three
quarters of a mile from Keld the track crosses the foot of Old Field
Hush Gutter near the head of which are the Beldi Hill Mines. The
Old Field Hush was worked from 1738 until 1846 when James
Kearton and twenty men made a bargain with the Beldi Company to
work it again. Two dams were made, one to the east and one to west
of the head of the hush and at each dam there was a hut to shelter a
watchman, on duty day and night, at each dam. As the dams were at
different distances from the hush there was an elaborate system of
signals so that the release of water was properly timed for the
streams to arrive together. In the bed of the hush there was a grated
pit which could trap much of the ore swept down after men had
loosened the vein in the bed of the hush. A tramway was built to
carry ore and bouse to the Beldi Hill dressing floors and then to the

smelt mill. The hush was worked in this way for sixteen years and was very productive. The remains of the waterwheel and crushing mill can still be seen.

On the roadside just before the hush is crossed there is the mouth of the Landy Level driven in the eighteenth century to cut the vein below the hush. Two other levels were driven at a later date. The Beldi Hill Top Level behind Crackpot Hall was started in 1773 and has a length of about 1,000 fathoms, with rises into all the principal veins. It was productive in the upper limestone beds and worked until 1880. The most extensive remains of the mines are at the mouth of this level below which are the large wheelpit and remains of the crushing mill. A Level, the Plate Holes or Low Level, was driven from above the river to explore the veins below the main limestone but very little ore was found. A rise was made into Landy Level and this connected it with Beldi Hill. This level was abandoned in 1882 when water from the old workings in Landy Level burst in and almost produced a tragedy. At the time only four men were working in the mine and two of them, S. Raw of Muker and James Allinson of Brierfield, had a narrow escape. After firing a shot they heard the rushing of water and realising their danger they rushed along the drift and down the rise. On reaching the bottom the older man pushed the younger into a tub and set off full speed for the entrance. The rush of water overtook them just as they got near daylight and before they got safely out it was running to half the height of the level. This water-burst filled the rise with stones and rubbish and completely destroyed this part of the workings.

We can continue the walk to Swinnergill where the ruins of the Beldi Hill Smelt Mill built in 1771, stand near the junction of the beck with the Swale. The Swinnergill Mines are half a mile up the gill and on the way to them, on the west side of the stream, is the old Parkes Level (1746). It was leased by the A.D. Company in 1873 and they put rails in it for 240 fathoms, then drove it forward for some distance but the veins it cut proved too poor at that depth and it was abandoned in 1878. Swinnergill Mines are on the east of the gill where East Grain joins it, and are marked by dressing floors and the ruins of a smelt mill. Before following this complex to the east there is another small group of mines on the east side of the Swale midway between Swinnergill mouth and Muker. These are the Arngill Mines on the south-eastern extension of veins which run from Keldside and Kisdon. (See Map 1, p 36.)

The documented history of Arngill begins with a lease in 1811 when a small partnership of local men drove a 'hand level' on a vein in West Arngill. In 1866 the A.D. Company re-opened this and called it the Eliza Level after one of Sir George Denys's daughters. It was still a disappointment as no ore was found. In the early part of the nineteenth century a level was driven in East Arngill to drain the workings on a vein that had been worked by shafts along its outcrop on the hilltop. A new and lower level was driven by the A.D. Company about 1865 and called the Adelaide Level, and this cut some rich flats and yielded a large amount of ore.

George Cottingham and his son discovered a rich flat of ore in this mine, which is said to have produced about £12,000 worth of ore. About 1918 it was again opened and another small flat was cut, which gave about thirty tons of ore. It worked for only two years and was then abandoned as the difficulties with water were too great for any profitable working.

Gunnerside Gill

The principal east-west veins of the Beldi Hill and Swinnergill Mines are continued to the east in an increasingly complex group which has been worked from Gunnerside Gill. At the head of the gill there is the very strong Blakethwaite Vein about a· mile further north. It is a strong fault throwing down the Millstone Grit to the north. This vein is worked for two and a half miles of its length to the east and for three miles to the west; it was proved from Stonesdale Moor Engine Shaft but was barren. On the east it reaches into the Punchard Gill area. The Friarfold complex crosses the gill at the Lownathwaite Mines where the main vein continues east as Old Rake through the Old Gang Mines. Many other veins fan out both north and south of this one over Melbecks Moor and Healaugh side with mines which will be described later.

The most important divergent vein is the Friarfold which goes north-east across the head of Hard Level Gill and on to the Surrender Mines two and a half miles from Gunnerside Gill. Veins associated with this are Reformers, Brandy Bottle, North Rake, Alderson's, Moorhouse, Freeman's and many others which were all worked from the Old Gang Mines, all being rich in the Main Limestone and all thinning below that level. It will be easiest, in this

Surface remains at the Sir Francis Mine, Gunnerside, showing the air receiver and level entrance *(H. M. Parker)*.

Ruined buildings and tips at the Sir Francis Mine Gunnerside *(H. M. Parker)*.

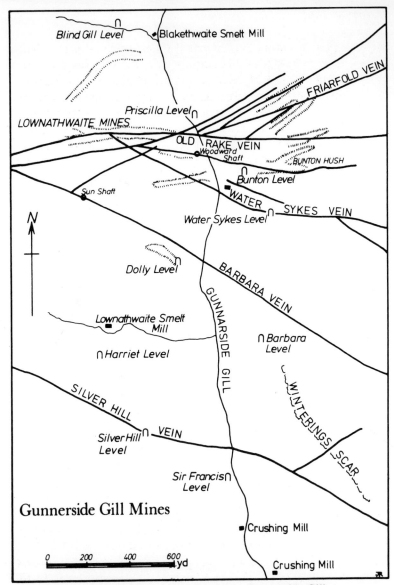

Map 2 Plan of the Mines, veins and levels in Gunnerside Gill.

complex ground, to follow the gill up from Gunnerside and note a few of the more interesting and obvious mines as we come at them. A mile up the gill from Gunnerside we come to Winterings Edge on the east side and on the top scar there are traces of several bail hill smelting sites. In the valley bottom the debris from two crushing mills, one on each side of the stream is passed just before seeing the Sir Francis Level on the west side, nearly opposite the mid-point of Winterings Scar. This level was named after Sir Francis Denys, the son of Sir George of the Catrake Level at Keld. The Sir Francis Level was designed to explore the ground below the Friarfold complex, to allow some lateral exploration in depth, and to unwater a large area. Several mines would benefit and the level would provide access to a good deal of new ground. Because of their joint interest the A.D. Company and the Old Gang Company combined in the work and cost of driving it. The Friarfold Vein had given rich ore in the Main and Underset Limestones so the Sir Francis Level was driven in the Middle Limestone below them, with a rise through the Three Yards and Five Yards Limestones between it and the Main.

The ground was surveyed and it was found that the level would be 43 fathoms below the Priscilla and 33 fathoms below the Sir George Levels. If carried forward to the Blakethwaite Vein it would cut it 33 fathoms below the Engine Sump which is 40 fathoms deep. Thus the level would drain the water from the whole of the Friarfold Vein complex and be of the greatest value to all the mines. The driving started in 1864 but proved to be hard and entailed very heavy expense, the first 202 fathoms only being cut by 1869 at a cost of £10 a fathom. Sir George introduced rock drills with a 38ft diameter waterwheel to drive a Low's-type air compressor to supply air at 60 lb/in^2. Dynamite was used after 1873 and the rate of driving greatly improved. Friarfold Vein was cut in 1877 and it was claimed that 550 fathoms had been driven in one third of the time and for half the money that hand labour would have taken. The Old Gang Company paid 4/5ths and the Blakethwaite Company 1/5th of the cost as the new A.D. Company was formed out of the older Blakethwaite Company in 1873. Good ore was found for a distance in the part of Friarfold opened up and after a short decrease came back and made a good mine right to their boundary.

To test greater depths a shaft was sunk down to the lower limestones with a hydraulic engine installed at the inner end of the Sir Francis Level, at a cost of £4,500. This shaft was 43 fathoms deep from the surface and cast-iron pipes bringing water from the

Cylinders and pipes of the underground hydraulic pumping engine in the Sir
Francis Mine. The winding cage can be seen on the right *(H. M. Parker)*.

Water feed pipe to the hydraulic engine, Sir Francis Mine *(H. M. Parker)*.

Air receiver for the Sir Francis Mine hydraulic engine *(H. M. Parker)*.

Sun Hush Dam were carried down the shaft to the engine which developed fifty horse power and worked both pumps and a hoist. The Old Gang also had a hydraulic engine in their part of the mines to the east. It had always been said that much good ore was left in the Priscilla Level so a rise was made from the Sir Francis and the level drained, but the report proved to be wrong, just another example of the innumerable reports of ore left within reach, but not to be found in later searches.

Large amounts of ore were got in the various workings along the veins served by the Sir Francis Level so two crushing mills were put

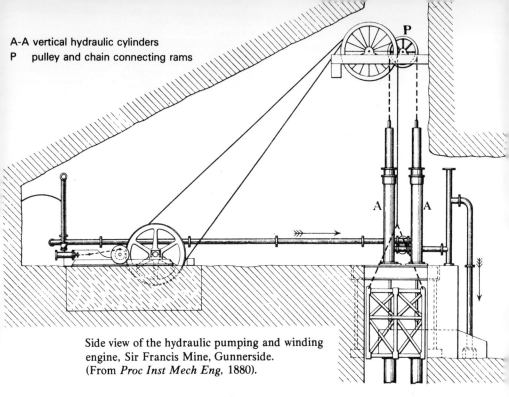

A-A vertical hydraulic cylinders
P   pulley and chain connecting rams

Side view of the hydraulic pumping and winding
engine, Sir Francis Mine, Gunnerside.
(From *Proc Inst Mech Eng*, 1880).

at its mouth and the A.D. and Old Gang companies had dressing
floors there. A waterwheel was brought from West Stonesdale,
28ft 10in diameter to power one of these floors. Up to 1880 the
A.D. Company are said to have drawn £32,000 worth of ore.
Dressed ore from the Old Gang floor was carried up the gill to the
Bunting Level, and dropped down a hopper at some distance in,
into the Hard Level workings. This carried it to the Old Gang
Smelt Mill at much less cost than carrying it over the hills. The
A.D. Company carried its ore nearly six miles overground to the
Surrender Mill.

In 1882 the price of lead dropped considerably and work at the
mines was almost suspended. During the stoppage the engine sump
filled with water and the engine never resumed work.

Near the Sir Francis Level the Silver Hill vein crosses the gill and
a level was driven on this at about 1,550ft OD. Another level, the
Harriet, worked this vein from the side of Botcher Gill. On the
north side of this gill where the road crosses it are the foundations
of an old smelt mill, the Lownathwaite Mill that at one time
smelted Lownathwaite ores but was abandoned about 1830. On the

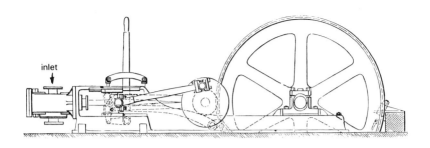

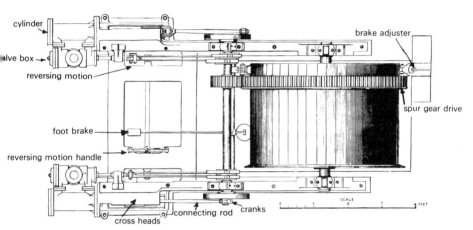

Side view *(top)* and plan *(bottom)* of the hydraulic winding engine, Sir Francis Mine (From *Proc Inst Mech Eng,* 1880).

opposite side of the main gill there is the Barbara Level on a vein of the same name, just at the north end of Winterings Scar. The Dolly Level a little higher up the gill and on the west side also reached and worked the Barbara Vein, and is a very old mine worked by Lord Pomfret in the eighteenth century.

Two miles above Gunnerside we come to the largest group of mines where the Friarfold complex is cut. Here the Lownathwaite Mines extend to the west until they meet the Swinnergill Levels. These mines were worked by Philip Lord Wharton from before 1670 and were taken over later by Lord Pomfret, and for a time by the London Lead Company. On the east of the gill the three principal veins also worked by Wharton, Pomfret and the London Lead Company to about 1770, are Friarfold, Old Rake and Merryfield. On the flanks of Gunnerside Gill all the veins are

Waterwheels at the Sir Francis Mine dressing floor, about 1900 *(Barker Collection)*.

Derelict waterwheel at the Bunton Level dressing floors, Gunnerside Gill, in 1925 *(Barker Collection)*.

marked out by large scale hushes. On the west of the main valley near the stream side is the Woodward Level with a very prominent high tip with a building on the top, and nearly opposite on the east side of the stream is the Sir George Level. Priscilla Level is just north of the big hushes. The splendid North Hush on the west follows the line of the Lownathwaite North and Middle Veins. Bunton Level on the east side has extensive dressing floors, waterwheel pit, and several buildings and is the general entry from this side to the whole complex. The Watersykes Veins were worked almost entirely by cross cuts from the Old Rake Vein in the region of the Merryfield Mine and were tried from Watersykes Level just south of the head of Bunton Hush. Near the Bunton Level there are some of the most impressive of the hushes.

Continuing up the gill past the Lownathwaite complex we come in a third of a mile to the Blakethwaite Smelt Mill and peat house with Blind Gill to the west from which the Blind Gill Level drives north in Blind Vein to cut the Blakethwaite Vein. This is about a mile north of the Lownathwaite group where Blakethwaite Gill bends to the north-west. On the right-hand side going up this gill the two Blakethwaite Levels are seen. The mine is an old one and before the levels were made it was worked from shafts on the moor top. The low level started in 1812 cut the vein in 1821 after a 400 fathoms drive, and the vein has been opened out about 870 fathoms to the east and 290 fathoms to the west. In the west workings a hydraulic engine was installed and the water for it was brought at first from Sun Hush Dam but later from two dams on Ivelet Moor called Moss Dams which drew some of their water by a long course from East Gill Head, several miles away. The finest survivals of this mine were the smelt mill and peat house, both very badly damaged by vandalism recently, but both still being impressive, especially the ingenious way the flue has been carried up the extremely steep hillside behind the mill.

Old Gang and Surrender

Old Gang is probably the mine best known to the general public and the stream-side near the Surrender Smelt Mill is one of the most regularly-used picnic spots. The mines of this area worked a great complex of veins where the group already described as the

The entrance to Blind Gill Level, Swaledale, showing a good example of
drystone arching and walling *(H. M. Parker)*.

Friarfold complex crosses the upper part of the Barney Beck, there
called Hard Level Gill. Barney Beck joins the Swale near Healaugh
and we can best approach the mines from that village. High Lane
runs up the south side of Barney Beck for a mile and a half, leaving
on the opposite side such interesing and grandly named places as
Dagger Stones, Thiernswood, Nova Scotia and passing not far from
Gang Hall. About a mile and a half up the gill a tributary,
Bleaberry Gill joins it from the north and a little above the junction
on the north bank of Barney Beck, the Surrender Smelt Mill stands
in a very prominent position. On the hillside behind the mill a
covered flue carried fumes to a chimney which is perched at a
much higher level on the brink of a scar made by the Main
Limestone.

The Surrender Mill smelted ore from many scattered mines,
from Surrender Mines and some from the Sir Francis Level when
the A.D. Company had it. It had a long history although the mill as
now standing was only built in 1839 to replace two very old mills,

the Low Mills of Philip Lord Wharton and of Sir Thomas Wharton, which were built in 1669 and had been busy ever since. These had served the mines from Lownathwaite along the whole length of the Friarfold complex to the Arkengarthdale boundary. The mines on the south side of Bleaberry Gill reached west from the ford where the road to Arkle Town crosses that gill and upstream from it are the Barras End group, chiefly interesting from their production of witherite for which they re-opened for a short time about 1920. Near the top of the gill are the Surrender Mines.

Half a mile up the valley from the Surrender Mill, under the scar of Smith Hill is the site of one of the High Mills of the Whartons, sometimes called Raygill Mill, but only slight traces of the foundations are now to be seen and are very likely to be missed except by the experienced eye. This mill, with a second Raygill High Mill near the site of the present Old Gang Mill, was at work in 1682 and the High Mill was used until about 1805. A mile above Surrender Mill we come to the most impressive of the ruins, the Old Gang Smelt Mills where the furnace house and many buildings, stores, and blacksmith's shop still stand but are all

Miners' iron tub from the Old Gang Mines *(L. J. Barker)*.

Ruined buildings and the entrance to Barras End Low Level, Swaledale
(H. M. Parker).

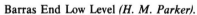

Barras End Low Level *(H. M. Parker).*

Entrance to the Hard Level, Old Gang Mines *(H. M. Parker)*.

The Old Gang Mines. In the top centre is the Old Gang Smelt Mill and in the foreground both rails and water issue from the Hard Level entrance *(H. M. Parker)*.

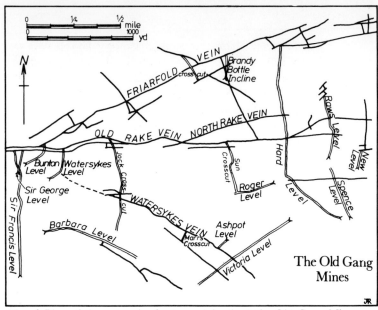

Map 3 Plan of the network of veins and levels at the Old Gang Mines.

ruinous. A mill was working here in 1771, the present mill being built after 1828. The position of the ore hearths can still be seen, though the fine masonry with which they were built was taken in the 1930s to be used in the new Methodist Chapel at Muker. There are two monumental features at Old Gang, the great peat store and the chimney and flue. The Peat House is about 390ft long and 21ft wide, its sides a row of pillars with open spaces between to allow the drying of the peat. The thatched roof has long since gone, but the double row of pillars and the two gables make a most unusual building. It could store sufficient peat for one year's work at the mill. The peat was used with a smaller amount of coal brought from Kings Pit near Tan Hill. The flue leaves the mill over a large arch then runs straight up the hillside for half a mile to the chimney on Healaugh Crag edge. The mill ceased working by about 1890. (See also the plan in volume 2.)

Just above the mill the mouth of one of the most famous levels is seen and the traces of lines from its mouth lead across a wide expanse of dressing floors with many remains of working arrangements, waterwheel pits, etc, still to be recognised. This is Hard Level driven in 1785 by Lord Pomfret as an entry to all the

Old Rake and Friarfold Veins. For some distance it almost follows the line of the gill then turns due north across the main group of veins. It is the entry to an amazing complex of levels which were linked up to one another bit by bit during the next fifty years. Its connection with the Bunton Level has already been mentioned. There are many levels in the gill, Spence's just above the mill, then across the valley to the west in Ashpot Gutter the big heaps of the Victoria Level are clearly seen, driven in 1859 to cut both the Watersykes Veins which proved very rich, giving about 1,000 tons of ore a year for seven years. Less than a mile up the gill, having passed the Herring Rake Level on the right of the road, we come to

Entrance to the Spence Level, Old Gang Mines. The peat house for the smelt mill can be seen on the skyline *(H. M. Parker)*.

the crossing of the Old Rake Vein with its enormous hushes. Just before this in the angle of two roads is the ruin of Level House which was occupied as a dwelling house in the late seventeenth century by Adam Barker, partner with Philip Swale and Philip Lord Wharton in the early mining. Baryto-calcite is present on Old Gang heaps and Smithsonite at Victoria Level.

Following the road along the hush to the west, you are going along the Merryfield Mines and the Old Rake Vein, with the Friarfold to the north of them, and in a mile and a half would come to the top of the Bunton Hush in Gunnerside Gill. Friarfold Vein has diverged to the north-east here and is a further half mile up Hard Level Gill, but just before reaching it, there is a famous mine, the Brandy Bottle Inclines. These are steeply sloping shafts, two side by side, driven soon after 1814 and they are about 100 fathoms long down the slope. At the vein intersection main levels are driven east and west and crosscuts join up with the Old Rake and Friarfold network. Half way down the incline a level takes off to the east and joins into the Surrender Mine a mile to the east which in turn joins with the Moulds Mine in Arkengarthdale. It was thus possible at one time to enter by Sir Francis Level in Gunnerside Gill and to travel through the underground workings through Sir George, Bunting, Hard Level, Brandy Bottle, Surrender and Moulds Mines, coming to daylight through the Moulds Level in Arkengarthdale.

Above the Brandy Bottle we see heaps of Bell's Shaft on the stream side just below the crossing of the Friarfold Vein. Followed to the east this rake brings us to the Surrender Mine taking us over a large number of old shafts and workings now partly grassed over, these being mainly on the Friarfold and Forefield Veins. The Forefield Mine was worked along here as early as 1670. The Surrender Mine is immediately south of these two veins and on the west end of the Black Side Vein which crosses the whole Arkengarthdale field.

An easy access to all these mines is from Gunnerside by a direct footpath crossing Brownsey Moor, with a short side branch to Kinning Level taking off at Mount Pleasant. At the highest point on Slade Head the path divides, one branch going to Old Gang Smelt Mills and the other to Level House, each about three miles from Gunnerside. Another approach is up Barney Gill to Surrender

Entrance to the Brandy Bottle Incline, Old Gang Mines *(H. M. Parker)*.

Looking up the Brandy Bottle Incline towards daylight *(H. M. Parker)*.

E

Mill from Healaugh, where a car can be left and all the mines reached within a mile or two on foot.

In Swaledale before getting to Low Row from Gunnerside there is an interesting group of mines, the Friar Intake. These are very old, being at work in the seventeenth century. The level just above the road and old shafts and a dam above it belong to the eighteenth century, when Abraham Fryer and partners were working it. In 1740 the Wharton trustees claimed it as part of the common in which minerals were reserved to them, but Mr Smith fought the matter in a Chancery action and he was awarded the mine as being with an ancient intake up to the boundary of the common. This trial was a foretaste of the Beldi Hill case. The Top Level was an attempt to drive into and to explore new ground at a depth below the old shafts, but after half a mile it was given up, the vein being too poor to pay for working.

An old tub in flooded workings at the bottom of the Brandy Bottle Incline, Old Gang Mines, almost at the junction with the Friarfold Vein *(L. J. Barker)*.

Arkengarthdale and Marrick

This field is dominated by two principal veins, the Great Blackside Vein which is an eastward continuation of the Friarfold complex crossing the whole of the area west to east, and the Stothert Vein crossing it and running south-east. In the west and east angles made by the crossing of these veins there is a large number of branch veins many of which were very rich in the upper parts. The Great Blackside Vein crosses Arkengarthdale and continues eastward through Booze and the Hurst Mines so that it can be regarded as part of the great dislocation which extends west to east from Keldside to Marrick and which is the backbone of the mining field. We have already noticed that the Arkengarthdale boundary in Bleaberry Gill separates the Surrender and Old Moulds mining setts but that these workings are continuous on some of the same veins, so that the separation of the Arkengarthdale Mines from those of the Old Gang and Surrender groups is only administrative and geographic and not geological.

The Old Moulds Mines are west of the road from Surrender Bridge by Foregill Gate into Arkengarthdale, and just above the ford through Bleaberry Beck the grass-grown foundations of the Moulds Low Smelt Mill, sometimes called Arkengarthdale Low Mill, are seen on the north side of the beck. The Moulds High Mill and Crushing Mill are about three quarters of a mile above the road, approached by a side road from near Old Bouldershaw House, now a barn, a quarter of a mile past the ford. Near the foundations of these mills are the Snuff Horn Shaft, Moulds Level and several bell pits and shafts on the Jacob Vein and its branches; half a mile to the north-west there are hushes, shafts and levels on the Great Blackside Vein, all these together forming the Moulds Mines.

In the triangle of ground between the Great Blackside Vein and the Stothert Vein west of their crossing and north of the Moulds Mines there are four strong veins: Black Jock, Dam Rigg, Sun and Martin. These veins are marked by a great number of bell pits and shafts forming the rich Dam Rigg Mines. The Dam Rigg Vein is the eastward continuation of the Blakethwaite Vein of the Gunnerside Mines. There are the remains of several dams which

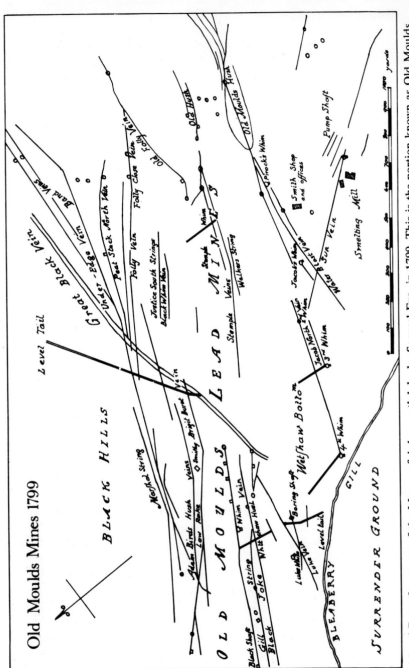

Map 4 Part of a survey of the Manor of Arkengarthdale, by Samuel Eva, in 1799. This is the portion known as Old Moulds Mines, on the west side of Arkengarthdale and adjoining the Surrender Mines group *(North Yorks Record Office).*

served not only the dressing floors, but also a number of hushes, one of them, the Dam Rigg Cross Hush, being the longest in the Swaledale district. At its foot there is the Dam Rigg Level, driven 200 fathoms before 1827 and cut 350 fathoms more. Half a mile west of it the Danby Level which is driven half a mile in the Undersett Limestone to the Joss, Martin and Nixon Veins proved very rich in the upper beds.

For half a mile round the crossing of Stothert and Blackside Veins there is the wildest and most impressive piece of mining landscape in the North. It is a maze of big hushes and open-cast workings on a very large scale where the veins have almost been quarried out, the biggest and most spectacular being at Stothert Hushes. Huge spoil heaps obscure many levels which open among them.

The general name of Hungry Hushes for this part of the area which is on the hill slope suggests that some mines were not as rich as was expected and this is certainly true of the lower levels. Down the steep slope of the valley side between the Great Blackside Vein and the Stothert Vein, now separating again, there is a large number of levels which are entrances to the deeper workings in this amazing complex. The biggest mines open from the Moulds Old Level only two hundred yards from the road and on top of the gigantic tips between which the road makes its way. Bands Level is more than a hundred feet lower and was unproductive as the veins were thinning out in depth.

There is a scattered group of mines opening from Punchard Gill and associated with the eastward continuation of the Blakethwaite Vein and the north-westward continuation of the Stothert Vein, which there changes its name to Cocker vein. North of the mines in Arkengarthdale and on the south-west side of the road are the remains of the large Langthwaite Smelt Mill built in 1824 to replace some smaller mills. Across the road from it and near the river was the famous Octagon Mill which had been the principal smelt mill of the C.B. mines since 1804, but this is now seen only as foundations and rubble. From the Langthwaite Mill there is a double flue climbing up the hill, joining the remains of the older Octagon Mill flue, and going through the Hungry Hushes to a chimney on the hill crest. The lower courses of this massive chimney and most of the length of the flues are still to be seen.

Stothert Hush, Arkengarth-dale.

Blacksmith's shop at the Hungry Hushes, Arken-garthdale.

The entrance to Moulds Old Level, Arkengarthdale *(H. M. Parker).*

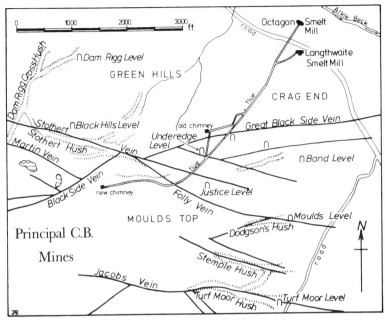

Map 5 Plan of the C.B. Mines, Arkengarthdale.

There is a long gap in the upper part of the flue where the twentieth-century chert mines removed it. The incline track down the hill and the curious deep-cut, walled trench approaches to the chert levels are still a curious feature of the area. The splendid Powder House of the C.B. Mines has been preserved in the angle of the road going down the river bridge.

The scattered group of mines in Punchard Gill are on the Bishop Vein, a part of the Blakethwaite-Dam Rigg Vein on which there are two shafts. Between these and the Cocker Vein there is another short vein also called Cocker. In great Punchard Gill there are three main levels: Routh Level, Fox's Level and Agnes Level. Near the head of Little Punchard Gill there are three shafts: Cocker Low and High Shafts and Bishop Shaft, and near the foot of the gill the mouth of Stone's Level is to be seen. This level was driven nearly due south in 1820, and unwatered much of the Cocker Vein ground and eventually reached the foot of Bishop Shaft on the Blakethwaite Vein. Much good ore was got during the driving so that it was not an expensive level, and after it was completed the portal was partly walled up so that it could be travelled by small barges which were used for drawing out the ore. Crosscuts and waygates were made into this canal from most of the Bishop and Cocker ground.

The powder house (built about 1804), near the Octagonal Smelt Mill, Arkengarthdale.

On the east side of Arkengarthdale there are three principal groups of mines, those of Fell End, Faggergill and Hurst. The Faggergill Mines are the most remote, but the most recently worked as well as having a long history. Faggergill is one of the mines mentioned in the earliest records but seems to have dropped out of the records until well into the nineteenth century when a group of workings was developed around the head of Eskeleth Gill. The Eskeleth Beck joins the Arkle Beck from the east just opposite the Octagon Mill site and from Eskeleth Bridge over the Arkle a road goes up the gill to Stang and forward to Barnard Castle. It has sometimes been suggested that part of this road is of Roman date but this is doubtfull though it was an important road throughout the Middle Ages and later. All the mines near this track have a long history. Along this road the first group of mines is around the Stang Level with the remains of large dressing floors in the hollow on the west of the road. The level has run-in but the position of the mouth can be located and there is a large waterwheel pit on the floors. The workings were connected with the Faggergill Mine in the head of Faggergill a mile to the west, where the principal entry to the mines was by Faggergill Level. This by cross-cuts drives north into a complex of veins, the eastern end of which was explored from Hurrgill Shaft midway to Stang Mine. After a long and successful life the mines were closed about the opening of the twentieth century. In 1840 the Faggergill Level No 1 was driven under Hoove Hill, with a complex of levels said to total fifteen miles and said by 1903 to have produced 24,576 bings of ore. In 1908 the new Stang and Cleasby Mines Ltd was formed to take over the Faggergill area, with James Backhouse as manager. The old levels were re-opened, Stang Level was made into a horse level more than a mile long and two new levels, Sloate Hole and Nut Hole, were driven. Sloate Hole cut several small veins and flats and got enough ore in the first two years (about ten tons a month) to decide the company to make this into a horse level and to rebuild old dressing floors at Nut Hole with a tramway to the main dressing floors at Faggergill. The mines worked for several years with fairly

Pony and tubs at Stang Level, Faggergill Mines, about 1910.

Miners at Nut Hole, Faggergill, Arkengarthdale, in 1910 *(Barker Collection)*.

Miners at Nut Hole, Faggergill, in 1910. Note the simple 'jack-roller' to raise tubs up the incline *(Barker Collection)*.

good results, but they were not as good as was expected and closed with a drastic fall in the price of lead in 1910.

Another group of mines is the Fell End, Tanner Rake and Windegg group near Booze. The Windegg Vein runs east-west and has been worked in part by deep open-cast trenching and also by several short levels from the east side of the Stang Valley. Windegg Level is driven from a position about 1,500ft OD half a mile north of Eskeleth Bridge, from which easy access was had to several veins and a good depth of ground could be drained. The veins were Windegg, Cocker Rake and Freeman's. The Cocker Rake runs east into the Fell End complex. The Washy Green Level drives north from the head of Slei Gill into the east end of the Windegg Mines. The Fell End complex is intersected by Slei Gill half a mile above its junction with Arkengarthdale and is well marked out by a crowded assemblage of hushes, shafts and levels based upon the exploitation of three main veins, Tanner Rake (a continuation to the south-east of the Cocker Rake), North Rake which is the eastward continuation of the Great Blackside Vein and a third vein between these two, the Black Vein. There are many strings and cross veins as well. The veins of Tanner Rake and Fell End are deeply cut into by Slei Gill and these could have been known and worked at a very early date. The Fell End Veins are all marked by very big hushes the whole height of the hillside and they are also approached by the Sun Gutter Level on the stream side on Primrose Vein Hush, as Tanner Rake is renamed east of the beck. A hundred and fifty yards below the Sun Gutter Level downstream and at the foot of the hushes there are the scanty remains of Slei Gill Smelt Mill (in 1729 called the New Mill of Farndale) but probably built as early as 1628. Humphrey Wharton was working the Fremington mines in 1679 along with part of the Copperthwaite Veins, and this was the only mill in Fremington which he could use. It might be as early as 1628, at which date there is an account for bellows and utensils. In 1729 it was sold to Charles Bathurst and used for Tanner Rake ores (Tanner Rake is in Arkengarthdale manor) and Fell End ores for much of the eighteenth century.

These Fell End and associated mines were worked for many centuries and in the nineteenth century the Storthwaite Level was driven from a point at the mouth of Slei Gill, but proved that the veins like so many others were impoverished in depth. The ground

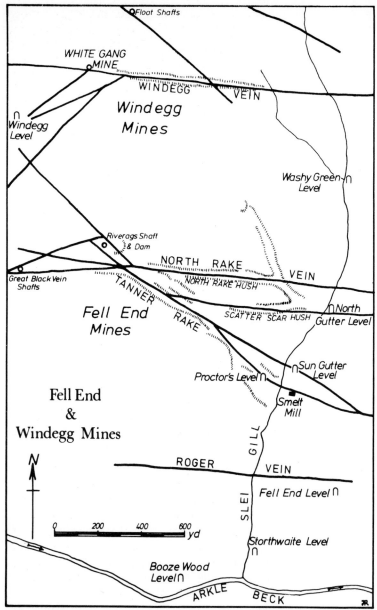

Map 6 Plan of the veins and levels at the Fell End and Windegg Mines, Arkengarthdale.

Fell End Hushes, Slei Gill, Swaledale.

Level at the bottom of Tanner Rake Hush, Swaledale.

below the Undersett Limestone, here about 500ft above the main valley bottom and so very well within reach and easily drained, was never worked. There is a fine level in Booze Wood, half a mile towards Langthwaite near the riverside which was driven north to Booze Vein, and which had a fine dressing floor and elaborate wheel pit in the mouth of Slei Gill with remains of an interesting tramway to it. The various veins of Fell End join towards the east to form the Racca Vein which, on the high ground south-west of Washfold hamlet runs into an interesting complex of rich, though short, veins which form the Hurst Mines. These centre upon Hurst village, though there is little to see now but an extensive welter of mine hillocks and the old North Hush and Sun Hush.

There is no doubt of the antiquity of mining at and around Hurst, but recent work has turned over the whole of the ground to such an

77

extent that all else is covered or destroyed. In 1814 the Hurst Mines were leased by Thomas Stapleton of Richmond and were then producing 400 tons or ore a year. After passing through other leases these mines were, in 1885, leased by Cookson and Company who had great good fortune with them and soon brought the output of ore to more than 2,000 bings a year. There was a dispute as to whether the duty should be paid in undressed ore or not and after a trial at law a decision was got that the duty must be paid in smelted lead. The mines closed down about 1890 after something like eighteen centuries of intermittent working.

There are only a few mines remaining still to notice on this north side of Swaledale and none of these form a group as big as those we have so far described. In the history of the dale Marrick and Marske figure prominently and both have honourable mention in the history of the lead mines. Marrick Priory had been granted among other things the tithes on lead ore, which just before the dissolution in the early sixteenth century were worth 24s, but about a century later (in 1634) William Bulmer of Marrick paid to the owner of the rectory £750 for the tithe of lead. This is convincing evidence that the mines had been developed on a large scale during the Elizabethan and early Tudor periods. From 1747 for a time the Marrick Mines were worked by the London Lead Company. There are two very strong veins in the area south of Hurst, Copperthwaite and Copperthwaite Sun Veins and these were worked in part by Humphrey Wharton in the seventeenth century and in part by the Marquis of Winchester, Lord Bolton. There is a great extent of bell pit and shaft working along them, and there were some rich flats on the vein.

The most impressive remains now to be seen are the ruins of the Marrick Smelt Mills and these are easily reached from the Reeth to Richmond road which goes through Marske and from which a footpath passes by the mills. Two and a half miles from Reeth the road crosses Dales Beck at Smelting Mill Plantation and the mills are on the stream side below this and about 400 yards from the bridge. There was a mill here in 1592. There are now two mills here, the older site being on the stream side, a small building 45ft x 32ft which housed two ore hearths. A later mill was built on the crest of the hill above the old site with two more ore hearths. Both were rebuilt more than once and the flues between the two were the latest addition in the mid-nineteenth century. Each mill has a fine waterwheel pit but it is possible that the wheel was moved from the Low to the High Mill as the flues are cut off as they approach the High Mill so the Low Mill must have ceased smelting then. There are three dams in the wood above the mills with a long water course from springs high up in the valley. These mills smelted the ore from Copperthwaite and Hurst and the ruined Cupola Mill, below the Reeth road, which had room for two reverberatory furnaces, may have been built to supplement them in the great nineteenth-century development. The east side of Dales Beck valley on Cleaburn Pasture and Cock How, is sprinkled with bell pits and just above the road and on the east bank of the stream an old level with an air shaft on to it was the approach to these veins in the later working.

Marske is an old mining centre and at Clints, there was one of the oldest smelt mills in the area, being leased with two furnaces in 1589. It was replaced about 1650 to 1700 by new mills at Clints Bridge of which there are extensive remains. On the upstream side of the bridge, below Orgate Farm and on the stream side there is a big tumbled extent of soil, rubble and wall fragments, with occasional slags, which mark the position of two mills shown on a map of 1759, each then having an overshot waterwheel, and a long water course the last part of which approaching the mills was carried on stone pillars. Below the bridge there are the rectangular foundations of the third mill shown on the map and this has a good slag heap running some distance along the stream side. The mills were smelting until near the end of the eighteenth century. On the fell edge east of them there are a few veins, the Orgate Vein and some of the veins which cross the top of Clapgate Gill. These were worked for the Clints Mills. Beyond them on Feldom Moor there is a strong vein which carried copper as well as lead and at various times from the seventeenth century was worked for both ores.

Chapter 6

SOUTH OF THE SWALE

The mines in Oxnop Gill, first leased in the seventeenth century have been mentioned in a previous chapter, and in 1700 the original lease was considerably extended to the west to include the whole of Keldside. There are however in that extended area no mines of a large size or much interest, the veins being widely scattered. The western end of the Friarfold complex lies in this area but is not comparable for strength with its central parts. A vein branches south-east from this complex and runs up the east side of Cliffe Beck as the Lover Gill Vein. This was worked in the opening of the eighteenth century but was then called Glover Gill Mine. Its equipment was listed in 1715 and included several 'Rowles' (jack rollers) with kibbles, thirty-nine shovels, picks and bars, with washing tubs, a buddle and buckers. There were the bellows, anvil and tools of a blacksmith's shop, the whole being a self-contained mine and dressing floor. The workings cut some flats and with work on a neighbouring vein, the Providence Vein was worked into the nineteenth century.

The principal Spout Gill Mines are on the east side of Oxnop Gill, mainly on Satron Side with some very large hushes as mentioned in an earlier chapter where some of their history has been given. The Summer Lodge Mine is about a mile to the south-east of Spout Gill and is now seen as a long succession of bell pits and small shafts with one large shaft, running from the head of Summer Lodge Gill to the Tarn. Summer Lodge was for a long time an important mine being fairly rich during the eighteenth century with an important smelt mill where the road crosses the gill. In the nineteenth century it worked a while from the deep shaft and a level. There is another group of bell pits about quarter of a mile north of the Tarn which make the Dry Gill Mine. There is little to be seen at any of these mines except for the occurence of a rare form of calamine on their spoil heaps, though this is now becoming scarce. The smelt mill is now largely a heap of rubble, but its foundations can still be traced.

East of Summer Lodge Gill there are three important mine groups which are documented for several centuries. These mines were leased to Metcalfe of Nappa at the dissolution of the monasteries

and in 1584 to Lord Scrope. In 1628 they were granted by the Crown
to Humphrey Wharton along with the mines in Fremington. They all
lie in the parish of Grinton and after Wharton had mined there for
many years they became the subject of dispute and during the Civil
Wars were confiscated. In the rest of the seventeenth century and the
early years of the eighteenth, they were still subject to disputes. In
1733 however they were leased by the London Lead Company and in
1750 leased to new owners who developed them during the next half
century into rich mines. There are three groups among them,
Whitaside, Harkerside and Grovebeck and all have large hushes and
many bell pits.

The Whitaside Mines are at the very head of Crag Syke and Birk
Gill which join the Swale opposite Low Row. They are on a vein which
is the continuation of the principal vein of the Apedale Mines in
Wensleydale. This vein is joined by the Virgin Vein also from
Apedale and the junction area makes the Whitaside Mine where
there are some deep shafts and some levels, with several hushes. An
old road goes the length of the Apedale Mines and comes over the
summit as a bridle road which continues down through the
Whitaside Mines. In 1768 a part of the Whitaside Mines was called
Fearnought which proved very rich in the nineteenth century. Ore
from the mines was for a long time carried to the Grinton Smelt
Mill, but from about 1770 was carried by a good road through the
Harkerside Mines to Scott's Mill in Grovebeck Gill.

The Harkerside Mines are along the fellside around the upper
course of Browna Gill and are marked by some large hushes and a
scatter of bell pits. In the gill below there is a level and the remains
of Browna Mine, which was working in 1700. These mines have
generally been worked along with Grinton Moor Mines and have,
like so many, been the subject of frequent disputed ownership. The
next group of mines is the Grovebeck Mines. These are in the head
of Grinton Gill, which in this upper part is called Grovebeck Gill.
The mines are on the east side where there are six very large hushes,
a large number of bell pits, a shaft and a level. The traces of the
Grovebeck Smelt Mill which smelted some of the ore taken away
from the Spout Gill Mill during the Beldi Hill dispute, 1769 to 1772,
are on the west side of the stream just below the mines; there is little
but rubble now to be seen, along with a few slags. Below this mill, on
the west bank of the stream there are substantial remains of two

Whitaside Hush, Swaledale.

Whitaside Mine, Swaledale, with the entrance to the Smithy Level inside the blacksmith's shop.

Waterwheel pit at the ore crushing mill, Whitaside Mine, Swaledale.

more smelt mills, New Mill and Scott's Mill, with water courses and dams, foundations and slag heaps. These mills for much of the nineteenth century smelted the Harkerside, Whitaside and Grovebeck ores. (See also plan in volume 2.)

Grinton Mines are mostly situated around the head of Cogden Gill and its tributary Smales Gill and are little more than a mile from Grinton. The oldest work was on the strong How Vein and along the whole length of it there are old workings and hushes and also two levels, How Level and California Level. How Hush, Ridley Hush and Swinton Hush are all very impressive. Cart Wheel Hush is higher up nearer the boundary with Wensleydale where at Height of Greets there is High Greet Shaft, and not far away at the south-west end of the How Vein there is the Low Greet Shaft, well inside the Apedale ground. At the junction of Smales Gill and Cogden Gill there is the Grinton Smelt Mill, one of the best preserved, the old mill having been more than once rebuilt. If we follow up the road past Grinton Lodge (now the Youth Hostel) the road approaches the stream just before the zig-zag bend over Cogden Beck and on the east bank there can be seen Cogden Gill Level driven onto the Great Stork Vein.

Half a mile above the smelt mill the heaps of the Devis Level are very prominent, the level leading into a maze of workings. This level cuts the Wellington Vein where it is crossed by two others, Robinson's Vein, south-east, and the Crina Bottom Vein, south-south-east. The latter vein crosses into Wensleydale becoming the great Chaytor Rake of the Keld Head Mines. Devis Level became a very rich mine in the nineteenth century. On the west side of Cogden Heugh there is still another vein with a few old shafts, the Old Stork Vein, but this soon crosses the Great Stork Vein at Heugh Nick on the Ellerton boundary. After this it takes the name of Redway Head Vein. After crossing the Wellington Vein it continues parallel to Crina Bottom Vein into Wensleydale. The course of these veins is easily followed by the rows of old bell pits and there is a big shaft at the Wellington Vein crossing where they make an important part of the Ellerton Mines. The Old Stork Vein has been very important in these mines, along with James Raw's Vein, all marked out by rows of bell pits. Two levels, Hags Gill Level and East Level approach them from the north. Ellerton Smelt Mill, with the very massive foundations of several buildings, is on the river side at the bottom of Mill Hills Lane which goes down to the ford across the river to Marrick. Philip Lord Wharton smelted some of his ores at Ellerton Mill in the 1680s at which time it had an ore hearth and a slag hearth.

Old Stork Vein continues east across Stainton Moor where, with two cross veins, it was worked in the eighteenth century from shallow shafts and later from two levels, Dagget's and Wyville Levels. Mining had started on Stainton Moor in 1680 and ore from the mines was, at that period, sent to many mills for smelting, Clints, Ellerton, Braithwaite and Preston. Its own mill was built in 1786 in the head of Stainton Gill and the foundations are still to be seen. East of the Stainton Moor Mines there was a trial made in Downham at a very early date and in 1675 veins on Thorpe Edge in Hudswell were worked for a time and their ore was smelted at Waitwith Mill which is now buried under the centre part of Catterick Camp. These mines worked intermittently but never with much result. The last attempt to work on Stainton Moor was made by the Stainton Moor Lead Mining Company in 1880 but without success.

WENSLEYDALE: North of the river

The larger lead mines are confined to the north side of the valley with only small, almost negligible mines south of the river. Those on the north side are mostly located on veins which extend south-eastward out of Swaledale. The Glover Gill Vein on the east side of the Buttertubs valley, mined by the Whartons before 1715 runs south-east from a major east-west fault which is parallel to and south of the great Friarfold complex. The Glover Gill Vein extends across the watershed just east of Lovely Seat and then is again mineralised and has been worked for a length of a mile from the Sargill Mine on the Stags Fell part of Abbotside Common. The Sargill Smelt Mill is on the stream side quarter of a mile south-east of the level and is nearly complete with a short flue to a stumpy chimney. The mine was working in the nineteenth century until 1870. The London Lead Company had the lease of this area from Edward Wortley in 1734 and their minutes mention a mine on Staggs Fell in 1738, which is later called Sargill. The smelt mill was only built about 1840 before which time Sargill ore was carried over the hill to be smelted at Summer Lodge.

The next group of mines is on Askrigg Common near the watershed east of the Askrigg to Muker road where two long strings of bell pits make the Beezy Mine. These are on the extension of the veins which make part of the Stottergill Mine in Oxnop Gill. The ore from Beezy Mine was smelted at Spout Gill Mill. The mine was working before 1765 and continued into the nineteenth century. A few of the bell pits not grassed over have an abundance of a very unusual mineral — sheets of perfectly crystallised chalybeate (iron carbonate) have been entirely replaced by hematite, but retain the wonderfully-sharp crystal forms of the original mineral. The whole is of a rich chocolate colour and the shafts where it occurs can be seen from a distance as dark brown heaps.

In 1670 a group of local yeomen bought from Bainbridge manor the royalties of Woodhall manor and opened mines in Birken Gill. These are on the southern end of a vein which extends south-east from Oxnop. The mines are less than half a mile above Woodhall, and were soon claimed by Lord Scrope but fights on the mine and in the courts during the next few years resulted in defeat for Lord Scrope. The mines continued working in a small way until the mid-nineteenth century, but the remains are negligible.

There is an important group of mines on the Woodhall-Carperby boundary around Disher Force and Oxclose. There are two levels in the foot of the imposing scar of Haw Bank and on Oxclose Pasture there is the very interesting Wet Groves Mine in the face of Ivy Scar. Here a rich vein has been worked in large open cuts and in small caverns, and offers a splendid chance to study vein mineralisation in the open air. The spoil heaps are rich in good specimens of baryte and fluorite, and hydrozincite also occurs but not so abundantly. The larger level at the foot of Haw Bank was begun in 1765 to drain the mines. The mines were leased in 1754 but were then very old. New levels were driven and fresh ground was opened by the Wetgroves Mining Company in and after 1859. The mineralisation spreads in a number of veins over a wide belt and some have been worked by very large hushes above Ivy Scar. Higher up the fell a large working was made on the vein at Thackthwaite Mine which was exploited by a level with extensive dressing floors at its mouth. This is on Brownfield Vein, one of the southward extensions from the group

which form Summer Lodge Mines. About a mile above Woodhall
there is the very old Brownfield Mine with a surprising spread of bell
pits and shallow shafts. Most of the ore was got from flats and
strings in the Main Limestone spreading laterally on each side of the
vein and that is why the shafts spread over a wide area. The mine
closed about 1870 after working intermittently since the seventeenth
century.

There are a few small mines on Carperby Common; Brockholes
Mine and High Greenhaw Mine are the largest of these and were
both worked from bell pits in the seventeenth century and were
again leased in 1765 and at subsequent dates. They are best
approached by the Beldon Bottom Peat road from Carperby.
Brockholes has a single row of bell pits on one short vein but at
Greenhaw there are at least five veins and the bell pits are ranged
along them. North of these and across Beldon Beck there is West
Bolton Moor with Woodale Mine which spreads across the boundary
into East Bolton Moor, a part of Castle Bolton where there are some
very old mines as well as more recent ones. Leland writing of Bolton
Castle in 1546 said 'Ther to a place in a great Rok 2 miles of where
my Lord Scrope seketh for Lede.' There is room for speculation as to
which mine this was. Detailed accounts for Lord Bolton's lead mines
are preserved from 1663 and mines were leased in Carperby, Castle
Bolton, Redmire and Preston and this is in fact the area of the
largest mines in Wensleydale, the only ones comparable with those
of Swaledale.

The key area of the Bolton Mines is Apedale traversed by the
Apedale Vein, continuous from the Whitaside Mines in Swaledale.
This east-south-east vein has two strong branch veins, Virgin Vein
and Bobscar Rake, which run for nearly a mile and a half
south-south-east from it. The Virgin Mine has worked about a mile
of this vein where it outcrops on the high moors between Apedale
and Beldon, both by bell pits, shafts and a level. This is sometimes
called Virgin Moss Mine. The Virgin Level is at 1,485ft OD and the
Hill Top Shaft at about 1,825ft OD two thirds of a mile away and
this length of the vein proved to be very rich. There is much to be
seen and at the level mouth good quality witherite can be found
which came from the workings of a flat in the last years of the mine.
The Bobscar Mine is a very old one with a large number of bell pits
at the south end where the vein cuts Rowantree Scar, and may well

be Leland's locality. At the north end of the vein there is Bobscar Level driven in the vein. Much of its ore was got from flats. The ore from Virgin and Bobscar was carried down to the old smelt mill in Scatter Gill, a tributary to Apedale Beck. The foundations of this mill with two buildings, a wheel pit, extensive slags, a dressing floor and a water course are still to be seen, and there is an old pony track direct from Virgin Level, which comes by the floors on Bobscar Mine. This mill was already in ruins before 1850.

Ruins of the Virgin Moss Mine, Wensleydale, in 1910.

Apedale is approached from Castle Bolton by a bridle road which goes due north across Bolton Park and Black Hill, crossing Apedale and continuing to the summit of Greets Hill on the Swaledale boundary then down into that valley. Much of the Apedale section of this road is built up and roughly metalled and this was for the heavy

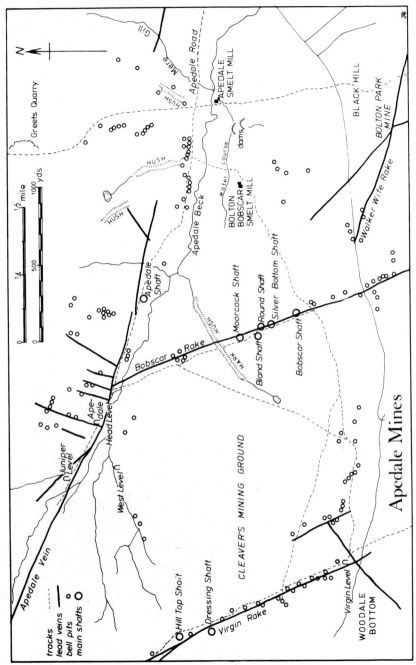

Map 7 Plan of the shafts, veins, levels and smelt mills in Apedale, Wensleydale.

traffic from the Greets Quarries, the stone from which was widely used in the eighteenth century and in the nineteenth was used, for instance, at Malham Tarn House. An old road goes up the length of Apedale from the Redmire to Grinton road and becomes a track over Apedale Head and down through the Whitaside Mines in Swaledale. It is a splendid upland valley, perhaps desolate to the eyes of a townsman, devoid of any outstanding features except those associated with its long mining history. The many hushes and innumerable grass-grown bell pits are nearly concealed in the heather. Remember that all except the bridle path are private ways and permission is needed before visiting any of these mines.

The path from Castle Bolton comes down into the valley bottom near the shooting hut and stables, having passed, quarter of a mile from the village, the Bolton Park Mine, a nineteenth-century venture and one of the last mines to work in the area. The shooting hut and stables built near the crossing of Apedale Beck are on the site of the Apedale Smelt Mill. Behind them are the foundations of part of the mill and extensive slag heaps. This was the old mill for Apedale and Apedale Head Mines and had been rebuilt and extended in the nineteenth century. In the deep gorge below the mill, which is the head of Bolton Gill, and a quarter of a mile east of the old mill is one of the finest levels, Harker's Level, driven about 400yd north onto a short vein which carried ore in the 12 Fathom Limestone. With a dressing floor at its mouth this is part of the latest development in Apedale, working until 1896. The Golden Groves Mine with a shaft is just above the road, not far east of the level. Going up the valley road there are several large hushes on the right, then in a mile we come to the impressive remains left by the Apedale Mining Company which sunk the Apedale Shaft here in 1868 with a fine waterwheel pit, four large bing steads and extensive dressing floors taking all the space between the road and the beck. Looking across the valley we see the long Mark Hush which cuts across the Bobscar Vein. A third of a mile further updale we come to the oldest and largest group of mines, the Apedale and Apedale Head Mines, where a number of short veins from the north run into the main vein and make some very rich ground. Here there are the Apedale Level and Juniper Level with Wood Pot Level across the beck. On the hillside above these levels there are many foundations and ruins of small houses which long ago were inhabited by miners who made a small

Apedale Head community. There are many banks and fragments of
walls marking old enclosures of the same date. The last working in
the upper dale was that of the Apedale Mining Company which
surrendered its leases in 1883.

East and south of Bobscar there is a group of very old bellpits on
a short vein, Walker Wife Rake, and running east-south-east from
this is the vein on which Bolton Park Mine was sunk. A little to the
east this joins the very important Cobscar Rake which runs due
east for nearly two miles, worked for part of its length in Cobscar
Hush and by a number of small shafts to Engine House Shaft near
its east end. Following the road, which is close alongside this vein,
near its east end we cross the flues which come from the Keld Heads
Smelt Mill and come to all that now remains of Cobscar Smelt Mill
which was built in 1765. It was enlarged and modernised during
the nineteenth century with a short flue and stumpy chimney but
ceased to be important when the Keld Heads Mill was built and the
Cranehow Bottom Mine ceased to work. Unfortunately this, which
not long ago was the best preserved of all the mills in the Dales, with
óre hearths, bellows and much gear in position and well preserved,
has now been reduced to a heap of rubble by army practice
manoeuvers and its plan can now only be recovered from wall
fragments standing about above the rubbish. Clough's plan and
Frank Woodall's photographs, made before the destruction are
now very valuable records. (See Volume 2.)

Only a third of a mile east of Cobscar is the last of the great veins
which comes south from Swaledale, here called Chaytor Rake. This
is the Crina Bottom Vein of Grinton Moor, very difficult to follow
through the wilderness of coal shafts across Preston Moor but
marked by occasional bell pits and by Forefield Shaft and Wide
Shaft. This moorland part of the vein is on army ranges and
preserved moors so it cannot now be visited. Half a mile north-east
of Cobscar Mill a length of this vein was worked in the very rich
mine of Cranehow Bottom. Two dams in the head of the beck
supplied the mine washing floors and then a water course went in a
great half circle round to Chaytor Rake again, near the Forefield
Shaft, to supply the large hush. The track from Cranehow Bottom
Mine dressing floors direct to Cobscar Mill was the only approach to
the mine. The shafts went through some coal seams and much of the
coal for the mill was mined from them. The Chaytor Rake continues

in a south-south-east direction for nearly three miles, almost reaching the River Ure in Wensley Park. This proved to be very rich for much of its length and in the mid-nineteenth century was one of the great mines of the Yorkshire field. On the lower length of this vein two levels were driven. The Keld Heads Level just above Wensley railway station was the entry to the great Keld Heads Mine, and the Ashbank Level on the river side above Wensley Bridge was the drainage level for the whole of the mine.

Chimney and roof of the pumping engine house at Keld Heads Mine, Wensleydale.

The Keld Heads Level and the scant remains of the big dressing floors 200yd north of Wensley station and the enormous spoil heaps which lie immediately east of them suggest something of the size of this mine. The west end of this area, near the cottages, is the site of the formerly important Preston Smelt Mill which the Keld Heads Mill replaced and which was at work before 1700. The tall square chimney stack which rises from one corner of the area is connected with a very impressive engine house from which an engine operated the pump rods in a close-by deep shaft. The pumps drained all the mines below the Ashbank Level.

Three hundred yards north of the Keld Heads Level are the remains of the once famous Keld Heads Smelt Mill with the Condesner House and the beginning of the flues which go up the moorland across Preston Pasture, eventually to join in the Cobscar chimney. Great lengths of this two mile long flue remain and show what a massive structure it has been. About the middle of the nineteenth century this mill shared with the Egglestone Mills of the London Lead Company the reputation of being one of the most advanced ore hearth mills in the country. Its processes, equipment and experimental work was quoted extensively in Percy's classic work *Metallurgy of Lead*. It is a tragedy that its destruction has been so complete and its few remains half buried under a quarry tip.

The Keld Heads Mines worked until 1888 on the easternmost extension of the mining field of Wensleydale, except for some very small veins about one mile east of Chaytor Rake. One of these, Longscar Rake, was worked for a time from 1760 by Lord Scrope and some partners, but never became an important mine

WENSLEYDALE: South of the river

South of the river there is no big mine but there are a few which had a short time of good production and the remains of which are still of interest. From the eighteenth century several leases were issued for prospecting within the Crown manor of Bainbridge but with little result beyond small trials. The first mine which has much to be seen about it, is Raigill about a mile and a half below Hawes at Hungry Hill between the Bainbridge road and the river. There is an excellent adit, a small mine 'shop' and a moderate spoil heap making a picturesque group. It is one of the early nineteenth-century trials which for a short time prospered on a 'flat' but closed when that was exhausted about 1855. There are numerous small trials on the fells up to Fleet Moss and a mine on Thornton Rust Common which employed two or three men for a few years, but it is not until we reach Aysgarth Mine that there is much of interest. A vein crosses the river from Ballowfield and Haw Park where it has been worked, and then in the fork of the two roads at the west end of the village of Aysgarth some small shafts and two levels were driven on it. Its life depended on small flatting ore bodies which were richer than the vein. There is little to be seen today except a tumbled area of grass-grown spoil among which a little rich purple fluorite has occasionally been collected. On the riverside above the High Fall at Aysgarth there is a level on to the Catscar Vein and a deeper level

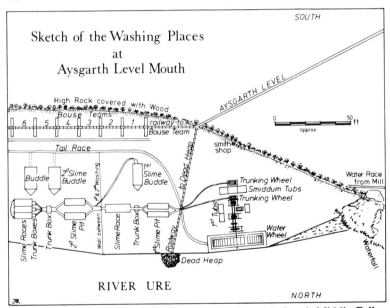

Map 8 Layout of the dressing floors at the Aysgarth Level, Middle Falls, Aysgarth, Wensleydale, about 1850 *(Barker Collection).*

from near the middle fall crosscuts to the same vein and forms Catscar Mine which for a time was very prosperous. Its main approach was by Aysgarth Level from the riverside at the middle falls. On a length of river bank an elaborate dressing floor was planned in the 1820s. It had a 30ft waterwheel with two roller crushers, trunking boxes, straight buddles, etc. There was a bank of six bouse teams, but little of this can now be seen. The mine closed about 1850 and only the eastern end of it has since been tried at the turn of the century. This was by two short levels at Sorrelsykes Mine east of the mouth of Bishopdale, but this had very little success.

There was little mining in Bishopdale except at the very head where the veins which form the Buckden Gavel Mine in Wharfedale continue north across the boundary and make the Bishopdale Gavel Mine. There was a rich flat in this vein and the mine was working on several veins before 1730. There is a very wide extent of mining ground with much open-cut work on a large scale, shafts and dressing floors, spoil heaps and at least one level. Among other minerals cerrusite (lead carbonate) and anglesite (lead sulphate) have been moderately abundant there. Some of its ores were smelted at Buckden High Smelt Mill in the eighteenth century. Waldendale is in marked contrast with its many mines and an important smelt mill near the village of West Burton. This mill has been variously known as Burton Mill and Braithwaite Mill and as early as the 1670s was smelting ores from Lord Wharton's mines, from Bishopdale Head and later from Braithwaite and Stainton Moor Mines. Its ruins stand on the junction of the road up the east side of the dale and the green road up Penhill, at Cote about a mile above the village. The mill with its waterwheel pit is now only a rubble heap but the short flue and stumpy chimney are there and should be preserved. West Burton Mine is at the village across the beck from the corn mill with a level (with a dangerous 32 fathom sump) and a shaft. In 1864 it produced 400 tons of ore from a flat and was a comparatively rich mine for a short time. In Waldendale there are many widely scattered small mines but only a few, Cowstone Beck Head, Dovescar Moss and Caldbergh, were really prosperous for a short time on flats of ore, while others such as Chance Hill, Walden Head and a dozen others were nothing more than disappointing trials.

In Coverdale there was one old and at one time successful venture at Braithwaite Mine near Braithwaite Hall. This mine was working in 1670 and smelting at the Burton Mill which thus for time got its name of Braithwaite Mill. In the 1850s the mine cut a flat and much ore was got with a sufficiently high content of silver to make it profitable to send it for refining to the Bollihope Mill of the London Lead Company, in Weardale, where above 1,500 ounces of silver were produced. The mine finally closed in 1866. Pumps at the mine which is some distance from the river were operated by a large waterwheel on the river side, through wooden rods suspended on timber triangles. There are still some impressive structures and remains connected with this mechanical system and these are well worth a visit. As in Waldendale there are some trials on very short veins, but none of them were really successful, except Gammersgill Mine on Carlton Moor where a level and shaft found a good flat which was worked until 1845. The trials around Coverdale Head were less successful with only traces of ore but nothing to make a mine.

Chapter 7

COPPER MINES AND COLLIERIES

Besides lead both iron and copper have been mined in the dales, but iron was never worked for more than occasional and widely scattered mediaeval bloomeries. Copper however was mined and smelted at a few localities on the fringe of the lead field and for completeness they deserve a brief mention. Two mines in particular were important, one with a long history and the other with a short but very productive life.

The 'copper mine of Richmond' mentioned in a charter of Edward IV, 1454, presents a problem as to its actual location. Clarkson in his *History of Richmond* in 1814, has confused the issue by saying 'a Mine of Copper near the very City of Richmond' with no more detail than just that. He quoted later leases of 1668 and 1697 which were of lead mines in the Town Pasture of Whitcliffe or Whitcliffe Wood and a later lease of these mines in 1718 mentions the royalty to be paid on both lead and copper. In 1750 he says 'a little time since these working were renewed [lease of 1740] but now discontinued.' On the south bank of the Swale near Richmond there is a trial adit with a small spoil heap, which has been driven on a short vein which carried both lead and copper ores in its spars, and this is marked on the Ordnance Survey maps as 'copper mine'. It is clear that it cannot have been more than a trial and also it is in Hudswell while Whitcliffe Pasture and Woods are north of the river in Richmond. There is a small lead mine above Applegarth, in Whitcliffe Wood which was worked after 1675 by Sir Thomas Wharton and had a small smelt mill at work for a time. The only copper veins however which might be considered are a small group in Gingerfield less than a mile north of Richmond town, which are in Whitcliffe Pasture. Leases were granted on these in 1763 which mention 'the old works', and the mines were leased again in 1863. The most substantial copper mine however is the one on Feldom Moor three miles north-west of Richmond where a long vein has been worked by bell pits, for copper pyrite which was smelted at the Copper Mill near the eastern end of the vein. This mill was at work in 1728 and then belonged to John Ward and John Appleby, 'lessees of the copper mines of Feldom'. In 1675 this was known as Washton High Mill and there is a slight possibility that Feldom was the copper mine of Richmond. Whatever is the true story, however, there is no doubt that from time to time for four hundred years, small returns of copper were got from this area.

The second and much larger mine was at Middleton Tyas four miles north-east of Richmond. This is on the Magnesian Limestone where, about 1750, in the course of opening a limestone quarry, calcite veins were noticed which were numerous and frequently carried irregular patches of malachite and other copper ores. A very small mine was opened in Goose Hill just south-west of the church but within two years, as the deposits proved to be rich, two companies employing miners from Derbyshire and Cornwall quickly developed two larger mines. The manager of one of them was Leonard Hartley, an active partner in the Beldi Hill mines in Swaledale. The ores were sufficiently rich to involve the sinking of large shafts and the erection of a steam engine for pumping. There was rivalry and disputes between the two companies and each built it own smelt mill. The details of one of these mills mentions two furnaces which were reverberatories. The ore was in irregular lumps and patches so that the workings were described as galleries in all directions 'and ought rather to be called fox-earths'. The maximum production was passed in 1765 and the mines had little more than a twenty-five years life of true prosperity. Remains are mainly shaft heaps at many places, a row of houses called Smelt Mill Houses, and the ruins of one of the mills on Cow Lane east of the village.

Other trials in the Magnesian Limestone at Kneeton, Leyton and Melsonby produced ore but not sufficient to pay for proper mining. Feldom became a viable mine on a long vein partly of lead ore and partly of copper ores, running for two miles across Feldom Moor. At the east end it comes near to Smelt Mill Beck a mile above the Hartford Smelt Mill. On the side of the beck just above Copper Mill Bridge on the Washton to Feldom road is the site of the Copper Mill. The extensive tips which mark the site are heavily grass-grown, but plenty of slags can be found which occasionally have small 'drops' or larger pieces of very pure copper in them. The Feldom mine is largely in army training ground and so is inaccessible.

There were a few trials for copper at the head of Swaledale and Wensleydale, probably due to the interest of Leonard Hartley. One of the largest of these is in the head of Sleddale west of Keld, and this produced a small amount of ore. Two others are in Mallerstang, one on the side of Hell Gill and one on Wild Boar Fell side above Aisgill. Just over the Westmorland border at Clouds north of Sedbergh and at Hartley near the head of Mallerstang coper ore in larger quantity was got and all these together were sufficient for a small smelt mill above Aisgill farm in Mallerstang and just on the county boundary. None of these had a long life and little remains but the dumps from which a few fine specimens of malachite and azurite have been collected.

Coal mining

Coal mining is very old in the Dales, being documented from as early as the end of the thirteenth century in the New Forest, Arkengarthdale. Coal was used for domestic purposes and for blacksmiths' and armourers' work in the early period, and for smelt mills, blacksmiths and lime burning until the end of the nineteenth century. The bell pits number several hundreds besides many deeper shafts and levels on the large scale workings. It is inevitable that anyone looking for lead mines will sooner or later come across old coal mines and unless the position of the coals is known, or by a careful examination of the material of the shaft heaps, he will not find it easy to distinguish many of them from lead shafts.

The earliest coal pits of which we know are those on Tan Hill, or Takkan Tan as it was sometimes written, where one of them was supplying coal to Richmond Castle in 1384 and coal was still being worked there in the nineteenth century. The chief outcrops of this coal are around Tan Hill from which it takes its name, where there are many pits. levels and shafts. Most of the principal workings in the nineteenth and twentieth century have been from the levels and deep shafts, most of the bell pits being earlier. Coal from these pits has been supplied since the seventeenth century to Appleby, Penrith, Brough, Kirkby Stephen, Hawes and most of upper Wensleydale and Swaledale among other places. The workable part of the Tan Hill coal seam, which varies greatly in thickness and quality over a wide area, is roughly that between Tan Hill and William Gill on the north, to a roughly east-west line on the south about two miles north of the river Swale, and from Punchard Gill on the east to the Westmorland border and just beyond in the west. The Takkan Tan pits were just striding the Westmorland border and were successfully claimed by the Cliffords of Appleby in the sixteenth century.

Moulds Gill Coal Level at the Tan Hill Colliery, about 1910.

There are four areas within which most of the larger collieries of the dales are found and in which the more important can be named and located. Over the whole of the dales however there are small 'coal shafts' to be found in many isolated places.

The first area is that of the Tan Hill Coal already defined. Only

300yd north-east of Tan Hill House there is a group of levels into the Tan Hill Coal and about 400yd to the north-west a group of older bell pits. The Tan Hill Colliery however covers an area due south of the house marked by a group of fairly deep shafts, Nook, Rigg and Clark's to the east of the Pennine Way and a few unnamed ones. There is also a long level, the Moulds Gill Coal Level into this area from Moulds Gill in West Stonesdale. The name Cinder Oven at the top of West Stonesdale reminds us that some of the coal was made into coke for use in the slag hearths at the various smelt mills.

A hundred and fifty yards east of the house along the Arkengarthdale road, here called Long Causeway, a green road takes off to the south-east to King's Pit Colliery, an old one which was sending coal to some of Wharton's Smelt Mills in the seventeenth century and later to Old Gang Smelt Mill. Among other shafts are the Smithy Gin, and High Gin. Branching more to the east from this road is another across Mirk Fell Edge where it is marked by piles of stones, to William Gill Pits, a group of bell pits west of the head of William Gill, about one and a half miles from Tan Hill. There is here the ruin of a small group of buildings, William Gill Houses, and some levels. Continuing east from here there is a fine track which runs along the very edge of Annaside Edge with marvellous views across the wide moors and gills of the head of Arkengarthdale. This road takes us to the Punchard Gill Coal Level in Great Punchard Gill which is about at the eastern limit of the Tan Hill Coal.

Due north of Tan Hill House there is an outcrop of the coal on the east flank of Taylor Rigg which is divided by the county boundary so that there is part of Taylor Rigg Colliery in Westmorland and part in Yorkshire. Also just over the boundary, due west of Tan Hill House is a famous group of pits which cannot be separated from the working of this coal, with pits clustered over half a square mile at the head of Wygill. These are Nab Pits, Kettlepot Colliery and Wygill Head Colliery. Takkan Tan is on the border midway between these and Tan Hill.

To the south-west of Punchard Gill there is an area in which the coal has not been worked, being remote and heavily covered by drift and peat, but in the head of Blakethwaite Gill on Gunnerside Moor it was worked for a time by levels and a shaft for use in the

Blakethwaite Smelt Mill. There is also a small outlier of the coal in the head of Barney (or Barnards) Gill in Wetshaw Bottom where a few levels won it for Moulds Smelt Mill. The seam nowhere compares with those of the true coalfields being only about eight to eighteen inches thick and rarely reaching two feet, though in one part of the William Gill Pits it did reach four feet but much of it was

The Entrance to Kettle Pot Colliery in 1921.

of very poor quality. The wide spread of coal working over this north-west part of the dales is shown by the frequency of 'coal' place names, Coal Gill and Coal Sike being fairly common, and others like Coal Force, Collier Gutter, and individual pit names like Hearne Pit and Hood Colliery with many others will be found even on the 1in OS maps.

Another area of collieries on the Tan Hill Coal is that on the south flank of Great Shunner Fell from Cotterdale round to Fossdale. On the east side of Cotterdale there is the Cotterdale Coal Pit worked from a big level and supplying a large area with domestic coal until well into the twentieth century. There were other small pits along the outcrop of the coal into the valley of Hearne Beck where the Tan Hill Coal outcrops at just above 1,850ft OD, the Pennine Way having passed many bell pits between Black Hill Moss and Bleak Haw. The Hearne Coal Pits and the West Pit Colliery are near the head of Fossdale Beck with a wide scatter of shafts, particularly on the west side and below Pickersett Edge. Across Fossdale to the east there are two isolated shafts, Head Rigg Coal Pit and Willy Coal Pit, but the Willy Pit is sunk onto a coal just above the Ten Fathom Grit and below the Tan Hill Coal.

Along the fells between Swaledale and Wensleydale there are several isolated collieries which supplied the farms and lime kilns during the eighteenth and nineteenth centuries. One very remote one is Cogill Head Pits on Abbotside Common at almost 2,000ft OD, in extraordinarily wild country where it could only be worked intermittently. The road from Askrigg to Summerlodge passes through the widespread Windgates Colliery at its highest point, where bell pits and shaft heaps will be seen on each side of the road.

East of the road from Redmire to Grinton there lies the largest area of coal workings anywhere in the dales. This is the spread of bell pits and shafts made by the Grinton Moor, Redmire Moor, Preston Moor and Bellerby Moor Collieries. The coal in the townships of Carperby, West and East Bolton, Redmire, Preston and Leyburn all lay within the Bolton royalties and was always worked by lessees, the earliest of the available leases being for the coal pits in Carperby, in 1569. In 1623 the coal of all the areas except Grinton was leased for 21 years to Sir Arthur Ingram who was manager of the alum works at Gisborough where great quantities of coal were consumed. There were further leases of these collieries in 1668, renewed at intervals until 1779 when they were taken by Thomas Southern and Peter Wilson Overend who was one of the principal lead mine operators on Grassington Moor. The Grinton Moor Colliery is actually the north-western continuation and corner of this wide spread of coal pits and it is difficult on the ground to find the boundary between them. The area of this whole group of

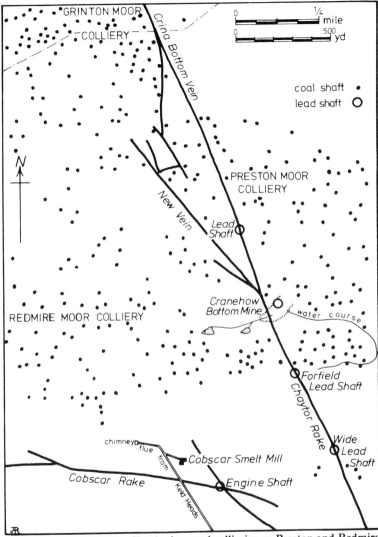

Map 9 The co-existence of lead mines and collieries on Preston and Redmire Moors, Wensleydale.

close-set bell pits is approximately two miles by one and a quarter miles. These pits continued to work until the late nineteenth century when the railway brought the better coals from the Durham pits into all parts of the dale.

There are scattered pits around Wild Boar Fell and Mallerstang Edge at the very source of the River Ure, and the Old Colliery near the Moorcock Inn was fairly extensive, working the coal below the Main Limestone as early as 1583. The very large Garsdale Colliery through which the Coal Road from Dent to Garsdale Station runs, extends across the West Riding border into a group of pits in the head of Mossdale Beck where there are shallow shafts and levels. A lease had been granted in 1742 to search for coal in all the common of 'Mosedale' and all the forest of Wensleydale on the south side of the River Ure, except for Raydale and White Birks. In 1783 a lease for 15 years was given for coal on Mossdale Moor followed in 1797 by a much wider one for lead and copper where found, and coal in any part of the moors or commons of Bainbridge and Worton. There is the curious but necessary provision that no mines are to be worked 'within the town streets, hamlets or villages so as to obstruct ways.' This lease was renewed in 1801. In 1819 the 'collieries, mines and seams of coal' between Greenside Road and Ten End Road (now part of the Pennine Way) were leased. There were repeated leases of coal mines in all this area of Dodd Fell, Widdale and Sleddale, during the nineteenth century with the mention in particular of Bank Gill Colliery and Storth's Colliery, which was only closed in the 1920s. The spoilheaps of the many levels are a prominent feature running on the contour of the coal seam around both sides of Sleddale.

To the east of the Manor of Bainbridge coals lower down in the Yoredale Series are worked at many places. The highest pits are those on Coverdale Head which occur over a wide area with several fairly deep shafts sunk in the base of the Millstone Grit. On Great Hunter Sleets there is a large number of shafts which are part of a larger area of workings divided by the Kettlewell boundary across which more pits form the Top Mere Colliery with many more shafts. A short distance to the north-east in Coverdale Head is Grouse House and around this ruin there are four deep shafts between the East and West Stone Gills. These are the largest shafts in the area. There are a few isolated shafts in the head of Walden and on the flanks of Whernside.

On the long ridge between Walden and Coverdale there is a well-known colliery, Fleensop, with coal shafts and levels which supplied coal to much of Coverdale for a very long time. There are a few old coal pits at Hollin Hole Well and a larger group south-east of Hindlethwaite with still more on Hindlethwaite Moor. A long 'coal road' connects these to Newhouse. Another fairly late colliery was formed by a number of pits on West Scrafton Moor. Though these are well-marked by bell pits, shafts and levels, and have served farms and lime kilns for a very long time, their history is obscure and only very detailed research might secure their story.

In addition to all the above there are many isolated coal shafts which for a time have served farms or lime kilns but few of them survived the building of the Wensleydale branch railway which made better quality coals available from the Durham coalfield. Only the lime kilns could continue here and there with the low grade coal of the lower Yoredales, and only these where coal and limestone were close together and could be worked by a single owner. Few collieries have attained a commercial size except those between Carperby and Leyburn, though others such as Storths and some of the Cotterdale and Shunner Fell pits, and especially those around Tan Hill, have had long histories and have been very important in the life of the dales.

Chapter 8

THE MINERS

So far our story has been concerned with the mines. The men who worked in them have received only passing mention. Many questions must have been aroused about the life and character of these men, and although there is neither time nor space in this account to give anything like a full answer it is right that something should be said about conditions in the Dales. Mining has always been arduous, dangerous, unhealthy work but the miner was usually a miner by long tradition and, as we say, had mining in his blood. This ensured a degree of enthusiasm and optimism, with patient endurance which is very much akin to the spirit of the adventurous explorer. The extent and content of a vein of ore is never properly known until it has been worked out and the whole process of mining demands the closest observation and deduction, the constant comparison of conditions, and judgements made in the light of past experience.

The constant pitting of one's judgement against the difficulties and chances of a vein, the making of bargains to work a piece of ground at a fixed price or the risking of capital in a mine, these are a gamble in which the occasional reward may be high but in which the sure expenditure is in dangerous labour and unstinted endurance. Generations of mining bred a race of men to whom such work appealed and in whom the experience, judgement and perseverance of many forebears was brought to the daily work along with the inveterate belief in the eventual 'lucky strike.' No other character could bear for long the conditions imposed by mining.

In all areas the veins, when explored in depth, thinned out and were poor, and this means that the richest mining ground, by the accident of the present topography, is found high up in the moors and in the valley heads. The villages cluster on the better ground of the valley bottoms so the miner usually lived a few miles from his work, miles which had to be walked over wild fells and moors in an area of frequent wild weather and a hard climate. There were fine days and nights as well as wet and tempestuous ones, but the mine was always damp, often very wet, and the miner rarely enjoyed sunshine on his early and late walks. Sometimes the brightness of a

An old stope in the Faggergill Mines, showing where the vertical vein of ore has been removed, with stemples across the stope for supporting waste rock or for climbing *(A. Butterfield).*

promising morning tempted him from his work for a day on the moors but these days were only few and far between.

In every way water was the miners' common enemy. He would as often as not arrive at the mine wet or at least wetshod; he might change into mine clothes at the 'shop' but at the smaller mines his clothes would be cold and damp and plastered with clay. Underground, water would be dripping from the roof, runnning on the level floors and in deeper workings threatening always to drown him out and sometimes succeeding. There are records of mines where, failing the capital or skill to install powerful pumps, the miners have spent as much as six hours out of eight in lifting water from the shaft in buckets to get to a working place. Add to the wetness the frequent foulness of the air in the levels and drifts, the oppressive darkness relieved for a few dim feet by the light of a tallow dip, and the complete isolation far underground and it will soon be realised that mining conditions were extreme in their demands upon the strength and endurance of the men who wrought in them.

Ventilation was always a difficult problem. A level driven far into the hillside or a drift taken from the bottom of a shaft was a dead end, and little fresh air could enter except with some mechanical help. The heavy breathing of the miner, the burning of his candle and often the fumes of gunpowder combined to keep the air foul. With almost continuous wettings, daily work in foul air and the appallingly heavy work on top of the weary trudge across the moors in all weathers, it is no wonder that the miners suffered regularly from the dreaded 'miners' consumption' and many died at a comparatively early age.

Further north the London Lead Company introduced the 'mine shop' system, where a changing house was built at the mine mouth in which a boy or an old man kept a good fire and dried the miners' clothes between shifts. At the more remote mines the shops were big enough to house many men who could bring food and stay there for five or six shifts, sleeping in bunks and having their food cooked. The shops allowed the miner to change out of cold and wet clothes to dry ones and to get properly warmed at the beginning and end of every shift. The ruins of these shops can be seen near many of the Dales mines and if one could only hear again the conversations that must have gone on far into the night, one could collect a fund of

Flooded levels at the bottom of the Brandy Bottle Incline, Old Gang Mines, showing the wet conditions under which the miners often had to work *(H. M. Parker)*.

incident and story unrivalled for thrill, humour and profound skill and knowledge.

Wages at the mines were never very high. Through the eighteenth century and the early nineteenth, an average rate was about a shilling (5p) a shift, or six or seven shillings (30-35p) a week. After 1850 this rose to 1s 3d (6p) or 1s 6d (7½p) a shift and by 1870 to 12s (60p) a week for daytale workers. A great many miners, probably the larger part, worked by bargain in the later periods. On this system the owner or company working a mine offered working places for bargain; it may be merely to produce ore, or to do a certain amount of level driving at the same time. The miners who knew the ground would bid for the work at so much a bing (8cwt) of ore produced, their price being checked or controlled by the company agent and by the bids of other miners and the necessity to get the best price they could. If ore was plentiful or easy to get, the price would be low, but in poor or very hard ground, or with very bad working conditions the price would rise quickly. If a miner got a good price for supposed poor ground then struck a pocket of rich ore, he was in luck and could make good money, but at the next bargaining the price would be adjusted. Much work was paid by 'fathom tale', driving levels, sinking shafts, cutting cross cuts and so on, being generally paid at so much per fathom. Daytale or so much per day or shift was more common among ore dressers and smelters. The large number of men on bargain work ensured that wages were always uncertain and subject to extreme fluctuation, so that most miners looked for some means of getting a little regular money as an extra and a standby.

Miners supplemented their wages in many ways, including poaching. It was natural that in their daily tramps across the moors, very often in dusk or after dark, they became learned in the ways of game and pitted their skills against the watchfullness of keepers. Tales of poaching adventure are abundant and the exploits of the poachers certainly added a little spice and colour to many hard lives.

Many miners rented a small piece of ground and worked it as a small-holding, perhaps keeping a pig or cow and growing a small hay crop. Many small cottages, now almost all in ruins, are dotted about the marginal land at the moor edge with 'intake' fields around them to tell of the labour of some now forgotten miner and his family. At hay-time in particular and at other busy times on the farm, some of the miners left the mines for a few weeks to work as

Brandy Bottle Mine, showing how the side walls have been distorted by pressure of the strata *(H. M. Parker).*

additional labour on the valley farms, making this their annual holiday. This was easy to arrange when most of the work in the mine was being done by bargain. The smelt mills used a lot of peat and a few miners undertook peat cutting and preparing in their spare time, as a little extra. Many miners found occupation as wallers. At the time of the enclosure awards many men left the mines to adopt the healthier occupation of walling and road mending, though this could last for only a few years.

The fairs and markets held a great place in the life of the Dales and almost all the requirements of clothing and supplies were got there. What little farm produce there was to spare could be sold there and agents were always in attendance to buy in the knitted goods for which the miners were famous. Knitting was a traditional occupation in the Dales and many of the miners were inveterate and swift knitters. Many knitted as they went to and from work. A common term for a short rest was to sit 'for six needles'. Stockings were the main product of the men's knitting, for which wool could be bought from the agents and the finished stockings sold either to the agent, or in some cases as part payment for groceries and goods.

Muker had a small market every Wednesday for clothes, meat and vegetables, and Reeth had its weekly market and annual fair which was famous far and wide. Fairs were also held at Muker and Gunnerside. In Wensleydale markets and fairs were held at Askrigg, Hawes and Leyburn. A visit to one of the fairs was an occasion for jollity as well as business, and the day often included dancing and only too often, some hard drinking.

Religion was not neglected and among the miners Methodism and other forms of non-conformity flourished. It was Swaledale where the early Seekers in the seventeenth century welcomed the message of the Quaker George Fox, and where Philip Swale, agent of Lord Wharton's mines, and many of his partners and workpeople became Quakers. Lord Wharton built Smarber Chapel in 1691 as an Independent Meeting House and in his later years established the Bible Charity which gave bibles and catechisms to all the children on his estates. In 1761 Wesley preached at Low Row where already a small company of Methodists was gathered. As in all mining areas Methodism appealed with great success to the rugged hard-living miners and small chapels were soon established in most of the villages, usually at great cost and personal sacrifice and with hard voluntary labour. The religious revival was followed by the stimulus of the Mechanics' Institutes and small Literary Societies. Libraries were part of these and books, occasional concerts, 'penny readings' and the many local brass bands enlarged the intellectual horizon and life of the people.

The expansion and prosperity which marked the latter half of the eighteenth century was already showing signs of decline in the nineteenth. Population had increased at a great rate and it was difficult for all the men to find employment. Housing conditions were very bad and food was poor and dear. A series of bad harvests between 1789 and 1802 started a vicious spiral of high prices and deterioration of diet which was continued by wars over much of Europe. In 1830 there was a murrain epidemic among sheep and agriculture was in a sad way. It was increasingly difficult for the large families to find a living in the mining and farming of the dales and it was then that the growing textile areas of Lancashire, with their insatiable demands for child labour, appeared as a possible relief to the local difficulties.

Many families migrated to Lancashire towns and as conditions improved after the 'hungry forties' more families were tempted away. Towards the middle of the century the mines enjoyed another period of prosperity, but this was threatened by an increasing competition from cheaper foreign lead which eventually combined with the greater difficulty of working the thinner and deeper veins to bring the industry almost to an end. By 1880 many of the mines were closing and population in the dales was declining largely by removal. Some families stayed on and small companies of miners from time to time opened up old levels and found occasional pockets of ore. In general however, the industry can be said to have gone into a permanent decline by about 1880.

We must reluctantly regard this book as the story of a past industry, rejoicing that for many centuries it had called forth a sturdy race of miners of high character and endurance, who have carried through many great works with simple tools, works which will compare with modern efforts. Machinery has improved, new methods of treating ores and metals have evolved, but the basic skill and judgement of the old miners has never been exceeded and we cannot pay too high a tribute to the work they have done. The few outward traces of their centuries of work are a sadly insufficient memorial to generations of sturdy Dalesmen who wrought in and loved these hills with an intensity which few of us can hope to equal.

Bibliography

Agricola, G. *De Re Metallica* (1556, translated by H. C. and L. H. Hoover, New York, 1950)

Barker, J. L. 'The Lead Miners of Swaledale and Arkengarthdale in 1851', *Mem NCMRS*, **2** No. 2 (1972), 89-97

Bradley, L. *An enquiry into the depositon of lead ore in the mineral veins of Swaledale* (1862)

Cooper, E. *Muker: the story of a Yorkshire parish* (1948 Clapham), Chapter X, 'The mines'

Crabtree, P. and Foster, R. 'Sir Francis Mine', *Cave Science*, **5** No. 33 (1963), 1-24

Crabtree, P. 'The Kisdon Mining Company', *Bull PDMHS*, **2** No. 6 (1965), 303-6; **3** No. 1 (1966), 63-7; **3** No. 2 (1966), 119-24

Clough, R. T. *The Lead Smelting Mills of the Yorkshire Dales* (Keighley 1962)

Jennings, B. 'The industrial revolution in Swaledale lead mining', *Proc BSA*, No. 1 (1963), 15-24

Lawson, J. 'Mines and mine owners in the central Pennines', *Mem NCMRS*, **2** No. 3 (1973), 151-60

Lodge, P. D. 'Hydraulic pumping and winding machinery, Sir Francis Level, Swaledale', *Mem NCMRS*, **1** No. 3 (1966), 21-6

Raistrick, A. *Two centuries of industrial welfare. The London (Quaker) Lead Company 1692-1905* (1938, second edition 1975, Hartington)

Raistrick, A. *Mines and Miners of Swaledale* (Clapham, 1955)

Raistrick, A. 'The London (Quaker) Company mines in Yorkshire', *Mem NCMRS*, **2** No. 3 (1973), 127-132

Raistrick, A. and Jennings, B. *A History of lead mining in the Pennines* (1965)

Memoirs of the Geological Survey. Mineral Resources, XXVI. *Lead and zinc ores of Durham, Yorkshire and Derbyshire* (1923)

Memoirs of the Geological Survey. *Geology of the country around Mallerstang*. Sheet 97NW, (1891)

Victoria county history of Yorkshire (1906)

Abbreviations
Mem NCMRS Memoirs of the Northern Cavern and Mine Research Society
Bull PDMHS Bulletin of the Peak District Mines Historical Society
Proc BSA Proceedings of the British Speological Association

Index

117

Keldside, 45, 67, 80
Keld Heads, 44, 83, 90, 91, 92
Kisdon, 34, 46, 47
knockstone, 27

lead merchants, 19, 20
lead ore, 12
leases, 19, 20, 30, 37, 41
levels, 25, 40
Little Moorfoot and Keldside
Mining Company, 45
Loaning (Lane) End, 14, 45, 46
London Lead Company, 14, 32, 41,
55, 78, 81, 84, 92, 95, 108
Lunedale, 14
Lunehead, 15

Magnesian Limestone, 11, 15, 97
Mallerstang, 15, 98
markets, 112
Marrick, 67, 78
Marske, 13, 14, 19, 20, 78, 79
Middleham, Honour of, 20, 30
Middleton Tyas, 15, 96, 97
miners, 74, 106ff
Moss Dams, 43, 57
Muker, 30, 37, 38

New Forest, 19

Old Gang Company, 51, 54
Old Gang Gill, 39
Old Gang mines, 44, 48, 57, 61, 62
open cut, 21
ore shoot, 12
ore hearth, 33, 40, 42, 62, 78, 84
Oxnup Gill, 32, 45, 80

pay, 40, 110
peat, 62, 112
plug and feathers, 22
Pomfret, Lord, 35, 38, 39, 55
population, 113
Powder House, 71, 72
Preston Moor, 16, 90, 102, 103
productive beds, 13
Punchard Gill, 19, 20, 48, 69, 71,
100

quarter cord, 37

Raydale, 11
religion, 112
reverberatory furnace, 32, 79, 97
Richmond, Honour of, 18, 20, 30, 96
Roman mining, 17

Satron Moor, 33
Satron Tarn, 33, 43
Scargill Moor, 14
'shops', 108
sieving, 26, 27
Sleddale, 98
slime pit, 28, 93
smitham, 24, 27
smelting, 24, 25, 26
Stainmore, 14
Stainton Moor, 14, 84
Stang and Cleasby Mines Ltd, 73
steam engine, 46, 87
Summer Lodge Tarn, 33, 43, 80
Sun Hush Dam, 53, 57
Swale, Philip, 31, 64, 112
Swale, Sir Solomon, 29

Tan Hill, 16, 98, 99
Tan Hill Coal, 16, 98
trunking box, 27, 93

ventilation, 108

wages, 40, 110
Waldendale, 94
water, 28, 33, 46
water course, 28, 33, 37, 39, 57, 90,
103
water wheels, 37, 42, 46, 51, 54, 57,
62, 73, 77, 79, 83, 87, 89, 94, 95
Wet Groves Mining Company, 85
Wharton, Humphrey, 30, 75, 78, 81
Wharton, Philip 4th Lord, 9, 27, 29,
31, 32, 55, 59, 64, 83, 84, 112
Wharton, 3rd Lord, 30
Wharton, Thomas, 31, 32, 59
Wharton Trustees, 35, 39, 66
whim, 40, 41
Whitaside, 41
Whitcliffe Pasture, 96
workstone, 42